Study Notes for Technicians

Physical Science and Physics Volume 1

John B. Pratley

BA, MEd, CEng, MIEE, MIElec IE

The Polytechnic Wolverhampton

McGRAW-HILL Book Company (UK) Limited

London · New York · St Louis · San Francisco · Auckland · Bogotá
Guatemala · Hamburg · Johannesburg · Lisbon · Madrid · Mexico
Montreal · New Delhi · Panama · Paris · San Juan · São Paulo
Singapore · Sydney · Tokyo · Toronto

Published by
McGRAW-HILL Book Company (UK) Limited
MAIDENHEAD · BERKSHIRE · ENGLAND

British Library Cataloguing in Publication Data

Pratley, John B.
    Study notes for technicians.
    Physical science and physics
    Vol. 1
    1. Electric engineering
    I. Title
    621.3   TK145

    ISBN 0-07-084858-0

Library of Congress Cataloging in Publication Data

Pratley, John B
    Study notes for technicians, physical science and
physics.
    1. Physics—Study and teach (Secondary)—Great
Britain. I Title.
QC47.G7P73   1984   530   84-9678
ISBN 0-07-084858-0

1 2 3 4 5   8654

Typeset by RDL Artset, Sutton, Surrey
Printed and bound in Great Britain

Contents

8 Properties of light rays

9 Chemical processes

10 Chemical effect of an electric current

11 Investigations

Software

Wherever the signappears in the text, additional material is available on an optional software cassette. Please see the back of the book for details.

Preface

This book has been written to cover the standard units in:

(a) Physical Science, Level 1, U80/682.
(b) Physics, Level 1, U81/845.

The book can also be used in part for:

(a) Physics at Ordinary level in the General Certificate of Education.
(b) Physics and Engineering Science in the Certificate of Secondary Education.
(c) YTS and TVEI schemes.

The aim of this book is to assist students by putting study notes, formulae, worked examples, and graded exercises into a compact form. It is a common practice for students following TEC courses to spend a lot of time making notes from information supplied to them by teachers. As they write the notes the students may miss part of what is being said, producing errors in their notes. This book is offered as one solution to this problem.

Problems, all to the appropriate level, have been taken, by permission, from examination papers set by the following bodies:

City and Guilds of London Institute	CGLI
East Midland Further Education Council	EMFEC
Northern Council for Further Education	NCFE
North Western Regional Advisory Council for Further Education	NWRAC
Welsh Joint Education Committee	WJEC
West Midlands Advisory Council	WMAC
Yorkshire and Humberside Council for Further Education	YHCFE

It is acknowledged that the organizations listed above accept no responsibility for model solutions, or answers listed, or modifications that have been carried out on questions. This responsibility rests with the author.

A feature of the book is that at the beginning of each chapter a list of SI units, symbols, and abbreviations is provided for all of the work of that chapter. It should make the students task easier by having a quick reference page to consult for any quantity, symbol, unit, or unit abbreviation that is used in the chapter.

Material from British Standards 3939 is reproduced by permission of the British Standards Institution, 2 Park Street, London W1A 2BS, from whom complete copies can be obtained.

The author would like to record his special thanks to Graham Saxby and Alison Watkins for giving support during the preparation of this book.

John B. Pratley
1984

1 Force and its application

1.1 SI units — symbols and abbreviations

Quantity	Symbol	Unit	Unit abbreviation
Area	a	square metre	m^2
Distance	d	metre	m
Force	F	newton	N
Length	l	metre	m
Moment of a force	M	newton metre	N m

1.2 Scalar and vector quantities

Any physical quantity that requires a direction to be stated in order to define it completely is known as a vector quantity. Force, measured in newtons, is a vector quantity because its effect depends upon its magnitude and direction. A scalar quantity, such as time, is sufficiently defined when the magnitude is given in the appropriate units.

Example (Fig. 1.1)
1. Draw vector diagrams of the following forces:
   (a) 4 newtons acting due west,
   (b) 5 newtons $\underline{|60°}$,
   (c) 3 newtons acting 45° north of east,
   (d) 4 newtons $\underline{|235°}$.

1.3 Resultant forces

The resultant of a number of forces is a single force that produces the same effect.

Example (Fig. 1.2)
1. Two forces, of 3 newtons and 4 newtons, act at a point and are inclined at 70° to one another. Find the magnitude and direction of the resultant.

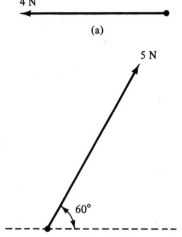

(a)

(b)

The direction is always taken from the horizontal in an anticlockwise movement

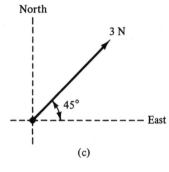

(c)

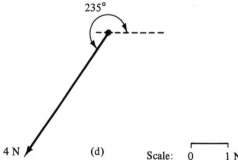

(d)   Scale: 0   1 N

Figure 1.1

1

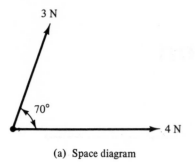

(a) Space diagram

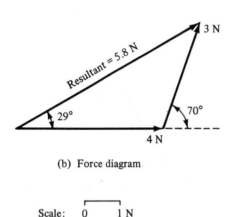

(b) Force diagram

Scale: 0   1 N

Figure 1.2

By drawing the vectors end to end the resultant force is represented by the line joining the ends of the vectors, and is found to be 5.8 N acting at 29°.

1.4 Exercise

1. Distinguish between the terms 'scalar' and 'vector' quantities.

2. State three vector and three scalar quantities.

3. Draw a vector diagram of the following forces:
   (a) 5 N acting due east,
   (b) 4 N, $\lfloor 75°$,
   (c) 6 N, $\lfloor 110°$,
   (d) 3 N, $\lfloor 200°$,
   (e) 5 N, $\lfloor 310°$.

4. Two forces, of 5 N and 8 N, act at a point and are inclined at 60° to one another. Find the magnitude and direction of the resultant.

5. Find the resultant of two forces, of 10 N and 15 N, at right angles to one another acting at a point.

6. Two forces act at a point and their resultant is 10 N, making an angle of 50° with one of the forces of value 12 N. Find the value of the other force and the angle between the two forces.

7. Two forces, of 12 N and 8 N act at a point and have a resultant of 15 N. Find the angle between the two forces.

8. Find graphically the magnitude and direction of the resultant of the system of forces shown in Fig. 1.3.

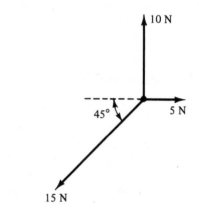

Figure 1.3

9. The following forces act at a point:
   15 N, $\lfloor 0°$; 20 N, $\lfloor 45°$; 10 N, $\lfloor 170°$; 25 N, $\lfloor 280°$.
   Determine graphically the magnitude and direction of the resultant force.

10. Find graphically the magnitude and direction of the resultant of the two forces shown in Fig. 1.4.
    (WMAC)

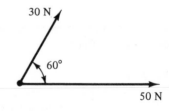

Figure 1.4

11. Find graphically the magnitude and direction of the force which must be added to the 40-N force shown in Fig. 1.5 so as to produce the resultant of 60 N at 30° to the 40-N force.   (WMAC)

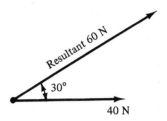

Figure 1.5

12. Two electric cables lie in a horizontal plane at an angle of 120° to each other and are attached to the top of a vertical pole. The forces in the wires are 150 N and 200 N respectively. Find the magnitude and direction of the resultant force on the pole.   (NWRAC)

1.5 Moment of a force

The turning effect of a force is called the moment of the force. An application of a moment of a force is the use of a spanner to tighten a nut. The moment of a force is proportional to the magnitude of the force and the perpendicular distance from the force to the pivot.

$$\text{Moment of a force} = \text{force} \times \text{distance}$$
$$M = Fd$$

Examples
1. Determine the moment of a force when a force of 25 newtons is acting at the end of a beam 3 metres long.

$$F = 25 \text{ N}$$
$$d = 3 \text{ m}$$

$$\text{Moment of a force} = \text{force} \times \text{distance}$$
$$M = Fd$$
$$= 25 \times 3$$
$$= 75 \text{ N m}$$

The moment of the force is 75 newton metres.

2. Calculate the perpendicular distance from the pivot when a force of 8 newtons is producing a moment of 80 newton metres.

$$M = 80 \text{ N m}$$
$$F = 8 \text{ N}$$

$$\text{Moment of a force} = \text{force} \times \text{distance}$$

Then
$$\text{distance} = \frac{\text{moment of a force}}{\text{force}}$$

$$d = \frac{M}{F}$$
$$= \frac{80}{8}$$
$$= 10 \text{ m}$$

The perpendicular distance from a pivot is 10 metres.

3. A wheel can be turned by a moment of a force of 120 newton metres. Determine the force needed to move the wheel if the distance from the pivot is 1.5 metres.

$$M = 120 \text{ N m}$$
$$d = 1.5 \text{ m}$$

$$\text{Moment of a force} = \text{force} \times \text{distance}$$

Then
$$\text{force} = \frac{\text{moment of a force}}{\text{distance}}$$

$$F = \frac{M}{d}$$
$$= \frac{120}{1.5}$$
$$= 80 \text{ N}$$

The force needed to move the wheel is 80 newtons.

1.6 Principle of moments 📼

The principle of moments states that when a body is at rest the sum of the clockwise moments is equal to the sum of the anticlockwise moments.

Examples
1. A beam 8 metres long is pivoted at a point 2 metres from one end as shown in Fig. 1.6. Calculate the force (F) required to produce equilibrium.

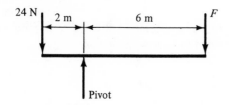

Figure 1.6

For equilibrium:

Total clockwise moments = Total anticlockwise moments

Clockwise moments = $F \times 6 = 6F$

Anticlockwise moments = $24 \times 2 = 48$ N m

Clockwise moments = anticlockwise moments

$$6F = 48$$
$$F = \frac{48}{6}$$
$$= 8 \text{ N}$$

The force required to produce equilibrium is 8 newtons.

2. A beam is pivoted at a point from one end as shown in Fig. 1.7. Calculate the distance (d) to produce equilibrium.

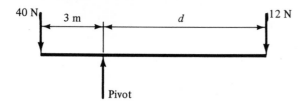

Figure 1.7

For equilibrium:

Clockwise moments = $12 \times d = 12d$
Anticlockwise moments = $40 \times 3 = 120$ N m
Clockwise moments = anticlockwise moments

$$12d = 120$$
$$d = \frac{120}{12}$$
$$= 10 \text{ m}$$

The distance needed to produce equilibrium is 10 metres.

3. A horizontal beam carries loads as shown in Fig. 1.8. Calculate the distance d.

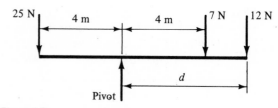

Figure 1.8

Consider the 7 N force:
    clockwise moment = $7 \times 4 = 28$ N m
Consider the 12 N force:
    clockwise moment = $12 \times d = 12d$
Total clockwise moment = $28 + 12d$
Anticlockwise moment = $25 \times 4 = 100$ N m

For equilibrium:

Total clockwise moments = total anticlockwise moments

$$28 + 12d = 100$$
$$12d = 100 - 28$$
$$12d = 72$$
$$d = \frac{72}{12}$$
$$= 6 \text{ m}$$

The distance d to maintain equilibrium is 6 metres.

1.7 Beam reactions

We use the principle of moments to determine the reactions at the supports of simply supported beams. After using the principle of moments it is useful to check by using the fact that:

Sum of beam reactions = total downward force

Examples
1. A load of 25 newtons is concentrated at a point 4 metres from the end of a 10-metre beam. Calculate the forces R_L and R_R as shown in Fig. 1.9.

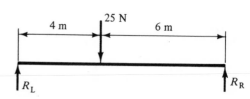

Figure 1.9

Assume force R_L is the pivot as shown in Fig. 1.10:

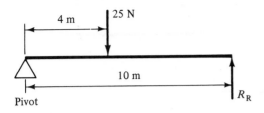

Figure 1.10

Clockwise moment = $25 \times 4 = 100$ N m
Anticlockwise moment = $10 \times R_R = 10R_R$
Clockwise moments = anticlockwise moments
$$100 = 10R_R$$
$$R_R = \frac{100}{10}$$
$$= 10 \text{ N}$$

Assume force R_R is the pivot as shown in Fig. 1.11:

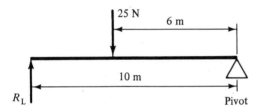

Figure 1.11

Clockwise moment = $10 \times R_L = 10R_L$
Anticlockwise moment = $25 \times 6 = 150$ N m
Clockwise moment = anticlockwise moment
$$10R_L = 150$$
$$R_L = \frac{150}{10}$$
$$= 15 \text{ N}$$

Check:

Sum of reactions = total downward force
$$10 + 15 = 25$$
$$25 = 25$$

The reactions at the beam supports are respectively 10 and 15 newtons.

2. A uniform beam 9 metres long is supported at each end as shown in Fig. 1.12. Calculate the reaction at each support of the beam.

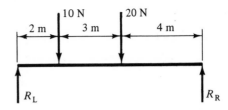

Figure 1.12

Assume R_L is the pivot as shown in Fig. 1.13:

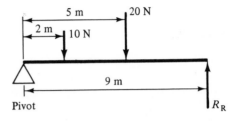

Figure 1.13

Clockwise moment = $(10 \times 2) + (20 \times 5)$
$$= 20 + 100 = 120 \text{ N m}$$
Anticlockwise moment = $9 \times R_R = 9R_R$
Clockwise moments = anticlockwise moments
$$120 = 9R_R$$
$$R_R = \frac{120}{9}$$
$$= 13\tfrac{1}{3} \text{ N}$$

Assume R_R is the pivot as shown in Fig. 1.14:

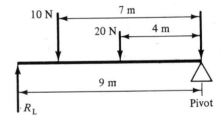

Figure 1.14

Clockwise moment = $9 \times R_L = 9R_L$
Anticlockwise moment = $(10 \times 7) + (20 \times 4)$
$$= 70 + 80 = 150 \text{ N m}$$
Clockwise moment = anticlockwise moment
$$9R_L = 150$$
$$R_L = \frac{150}{9}$$
$$= 16\tfrac{2}{3} \text{ N}$$

6

Check:

Sum of reactions = total downward force
$$13\tfrac{1}{3} + 16\tfrac{2}{3} = 10 + 20$$
$$30 = 30$$

The support reactions are $R_L = 16\tfrac{2}{3}$ N and $R_R = 13\tfrac{1}{3}$ newtons.

1.8 Exercise

1. Explain what is meant by the term 'moment of a force'.
2. Find the moment of a force which is produced by a force of 25 N acting at a perpendicular distance of 2 m from the pivot.
3. Calculate the turning effect of a force of 8 N acting at the end of a beam 3 m long and pivoted at its end.
4. If a moment of a force of 10 N m is needed to open a door which is $\tfrac{2}{3}$ m wide, what force is required?
5. A wheel can be turned by a moment of a force of 100 N m. What force is needed if it is applied at a distance of 1.5 m from the fulcrum?
6. A force of 150 N is applied at right angles to a spanner, at its end, while tightening a bolt. If the moment of a force is 30 N m determine the length of the spanner.
7. Calculate the distance involved when a force of 100 N produces a moment of a force of 130 N m.
8. Calculate the force F in Fig. 1.15 in order to maintain equilibrium.

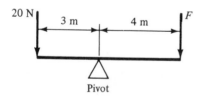

Figure 1.15

9. Two forces of 25 N and 36 N act on a beam as shown in Fig. 1.16. Determine the distance d in order to produce equilibrium.

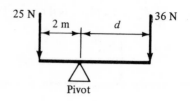

Figure 1.16

10. A uniform bar 11 m long is supported by a fulcrum (pivot) 3 m from one end of the beam, as shown in Fig. 1.17. Determine the value of the force F in order to produce equilibrium.

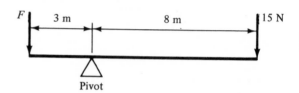

Figure 1.17

11. Calculate the distance d in Fig. 1.18 in order to maintain equilibrium.

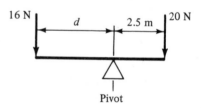

Figure 1.18

12. In each of the following, calculate the reactions R_L and R_R at the supports:
(a) Fig. 1.19,

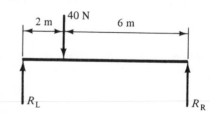

Figure 1.19

(b) Fig. 1.20,

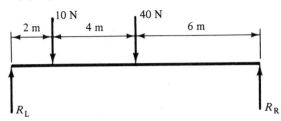

Figure 1.20

(c) Fig. 1.21.

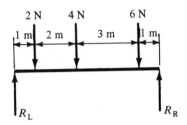

Figure 1.21

13. State the principle of moments.

    A metre rule AB, of weight 50 g, is pivoted at C, 40 cm from one end. A load of 20 g acts vertically at A. Determine the point of application of a vertical force of 10 g which will maintain the rule in a horizontal position. (EMFEC)

14. (a) State the principle of moments.
    (b) A horizontal lever ABC is pivoted at B. AB = 150 mm, BC = 1 m. The lever is of weight 5 N and the centre of gravity is 300 mm from B. A load of 30 N is suspended from A and another load of 1 N from C.
       (i) What is the out-of-balance moment on the beam?
       (ii) At what position would a load of 3.5 N have to be hung to give equilibrium? (NCFE)

15. A steel shaft of weight 20 N is 3 m long. At the ends of the shaft are two pulleys of weight 8 N and 16 N respectively. If the shaft is supported at one point only, where must this point be for the shaft to rest horizontally? (WMAC)

16. (a) Define the moment of a force and give suitable units.

    (b) A uniform beam ABCDE of weight 1 N is supported at B and E. The beam carries loads of 10, 2, and 4 N at A, C, and D respectively. AB = 2 m, BC = 0.8m, CD = 2 m, and DE = 1 m. Calculate the reactions at B and E and state the directions in which the reactions act. (NCFE)

17. Explain the term 'resultant'.

    Three vertically downward forces have values of 5 N, 4 N, and 6 N and the horizontal distances between their points of action are 100 mm and 175 mm respectively. Find the magnitude and position of their resultant. (WJEC)

18. Draw a labelled diagram to show how a crowbar is used to lift a heavy weight.

    Calculate the effort required to raise a load of 100 N by means of a crowbar 2 m long if the load is at one end and 0.4 m from the fulcrum and the effort is applied at the other end of the bar. (WJEC)

19. Define the moment of a force.

    A uniform lever 1 m long and of weight 15 N has a fulcrum 0.2 m from one end. Calculate the load which must be hung from the end nearest the fulcrum in order to keep the lever horizontal. (NWRAC)

20. Define the moment of a force.

    A uniform beam AB is 10 m long, weighs 1000 N and is simply supported at C and D, 2 m and 3 m from A and B respectively. Calculate the magnitude of the reactions at C and D. What is the effect on the magnitude of these reactions if a load of 400 N is placed mid-way between C and D? (NWRAC)

1.9 Centre of mass 📼

The centre of mass is the point at which, for the purpose of calculations, the mass of a body may be considered to be concentrated. In a uniform gravitational field the centre of mass coincides with the point known as the centre of gravity. The position of a number of thin components is shown in Fig. 1.22.

8

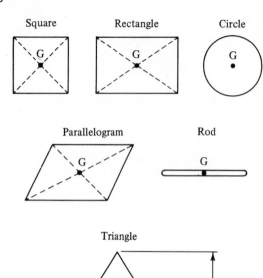

Square   Rectangle   Circle

Parallelogram   Rod

Triangle

Figure 1.22

In order to determine the position of the centre of gravity of a body we use the principle of moments, as shown in the following examples.

Examples

1. Find the centre of gravity of the thin sheet shown in Fig. 1.23.

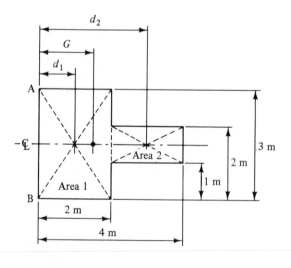

Figure 1.23

$(\text{Area } 1 \times d_1) + (\text{area } 2 \times d_2) = \text{total area} \times G$

where G is the position of the centre of gravity.

$$\text{Area } 1 = 2 \times 3 = 6 \text{ m}^2$$
$$\text{Area } 2 = 2 \times 1 = 2 \text{ m}^2$$
$$\text{Total area } = 8 \text{ m}^2$$

Take moments about AB:

$$(6 \times 1) + (2 \times 3) = 8 \times G$$
$$6 + 6 = 8G$$
$$12 = 8G$$

Therefore

$$G = \frac{12}{8}$$
$$= 1.5 \text{ m}$$

The position of the centre of gravity is on the centre line and 1.5 metres from the side AB.

2. Find the centre of gravity of the thin sheet shown in Fig. 1.24.

$$\text{Area } 1 = 100 \times 30 = 3000 \text{ mm}^2$$
$$\text{Area } 2 = 90 \times 20 = 1800 \text{ mm}^2$$
$$\text{Total area} = 3000 + 1800 = 4800 \text{ mm}^2$$

Take moments about side AB:

$$(\text{Area } 1 \times d_{1x}) + (\text{area } 2 \times d_{2x}) = \text{total area} \times G_x$$
$$(3000 \times 15) + (1800 \times 75) = 4800 \times G_x$$
$$45\,000 + 135\,000 = 4800 G_x$$
$$180\,000 = 4800 G_x$$

Therefore

$$G_x = \frac{180\,000}{4800}$$
$$= 37.5 \text{ mm}$$

Take moments about side AC:

$$(\text{Area } 1 \times d_{1y}) + (\text{area } 2 \times d_{2y}) = \text{total area} \times G_y$$
$$(3000 \times 50) + (1800 \times 10) = 4800 G_y$$
$$150\,000 + 18\,000 = 4800 G_y$$
$$168\,000 = 4800 G_y$$

Therefore

$$G_y = \frac{168\,000}{4800}$$
$$= 35 \text{ mm}$$

The centre of gravity is located at a point 37.5 millimetres from side AB and 35 millimetres from side AC.

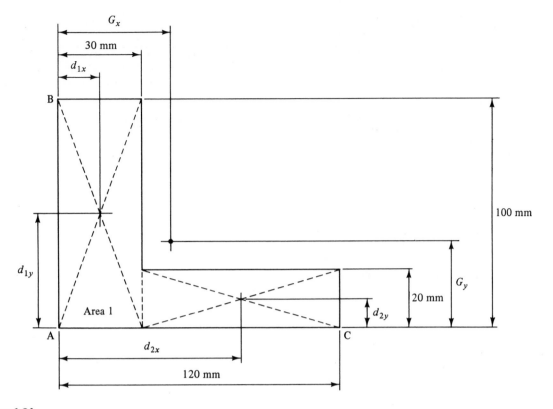

Figure 1.24

The results obtained by calculation in Example 2 can be verified experimentally. The centre of gravity is located by applying the principle that if a body is suspended from a point it will come to rest with its centre of gravity vertically below the point. Use a thin sheet of carboard and cut out the shape drawn in Fig. 1.24. Suspend the cutout from point A and when it is at rest carefully draw a line vertically through the point of support as shown in Fig. 1.25. Repeat this procedure by suspending the cutout from points B and C. The vertical lines will all cross at the same point which is the centre of gravity of the cutout. Check that the experimental result is close to the calculated result.

1.10 Stable, unstable, and neutral equilibrium

The equilibrium of a body when acted upon by a number of forces may be stable, unstable, or neutral.

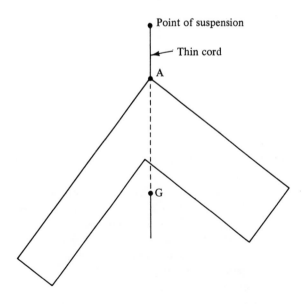

Figure 1.25

A body at rest is in stable equilibrium if when slightly displaced it generally returns to its original position of rest. If the displacement tends to increase and the body moves further away from its original position, the body is then said to be unstable. A body is said to be in neutral equilibrium when it tends to rest in any position it is placed. Positions of stable equilibrium are positions of minimum potential energy; those of unstable equilibrium are of maximum potential energy.

1.11 Exercise

1. Figure 1.26 shows a thin uniform plate. Find the distances of the centre of gravity from the edges AB and BC. If the plate is suspended freely from the corner A find the inclination of the edge AB to the vertical. (WJEC)

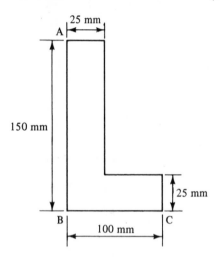

Figure 1.26

2. (a) Describe an experiment to find the centroid of a lamina.
   (b) Calculate the position of the centroid of an L-shaped lamina 200 mm high and 150 mm wide, each leg being 50 mm wide. (NCFE)
3. (a) Describe with the aid of sketches a practical method of determining the position of the centroid of an irregular shape of uniform thickness.
   (b) Calculate the position of the centroid of an L-shaped plate having limbs of length

125 mm and 75 mm respectively, each limb being 25 mm wide. (WMAC)

4. Draw, half size, a triangle whose sides are 30 mm, 40 mm, and 50 mm respectively to represent a uniform sheet of tinplate. Mark the position of the centre of gravity of this sheet of metal, showing clearly how you have determined the position. (NWRAC)

5. Explain what is meant by the term 'centre of gravity'.

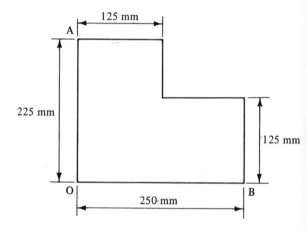

Figure 1.27

Figure 1.27 shows the plan view of a steel forging of uniform cross-section. The forging has to be lifted vertically by means of an eyebolt. Determine the position of the eyebolt from OA and OB so that the face OAB will remain horizontal. (WMAC)

6. Figure 1.28 shows the simplified cross-section of a beam. Calculate the distance of the centroid of the section from the axis XX. (NWRAC)
7. Figure 1.29 shows a thin uniform plate. Find the distances of the centre of gravity from the edges AB and BC. (WJEC)
8. (a) Briefly describe a method of finding the position of the centre of gravity of an irregular-shaped sheet of thin metal.
   (b) A 100-mm square sheet of metal has a 50-mm square cut from one corner. Calculate the distance from a 100-mm side to the position of the centre of gravity of the L-shaped piece which remains. (NCFE)

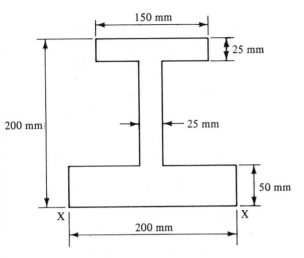

Figure 1.28

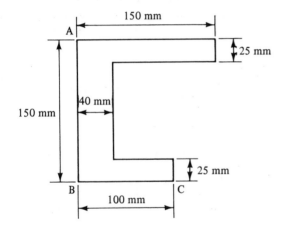

Figure 1.29

150 mm is placed on a 25-mm thick triangular plate ABC so that the points A, B, and C on both plates coincide. Calculate the distances of the centre of gravity of the combined plates from AB and BC. (NCFE)

12. Complete the crossword puzzle of Fig. 1.30 using Chapter 1 for reference material.

Figure 1.30

9. A uniform plate has the shape of a trapezium. The vertical parallel sides are respectively 100 mm and 175 mm long and the horizontal base is 225 mm. Determine the position of the centre of gravity of the plate. Describe how you would check your result experimentally. (WJEC)

10. Define the term 'centre of gravity'.

   A T-section beam has a width of 150 mm and an overall depth also of 150 mm. Both the flange and web are 12 mm thick. Calculate the position of the centre of area of the cross-section. (NWRAC)

11. A 25-mm thick rectangular steel plate ABCD having dimensions AB = 225 mm and BC =

Across

1. Opposite to east and in reverse
2. A body at rest is in . . . . . . equilibrium.
5. One point of the compass with the 'h' missing
7. The unit is a metre.
10. Un . .
11. A quantity with direction
14. A load of 25 N is concentrated at a point 3 m from the end of a 5 m beam which is simply supported at each end. Determine the value of the beam reaction at the left-hand end of the beam.
16. In a beam $R_L + R_R = 17$. What will be the value of R_R if $R_L = 8$?
17. M.gni.ud.
19. The resultant of a number of forces is a single . . . . .
20. Useful in the middle of gravity
21. The unit of a moment in reverse

Down

1. Same value as 14 across
2. Without direction
3. A beam goes . . . . if inadequately supported.
4. Calculate the perpendicular distance from the pivot when a force of 10 N is producing a moment of 80 N m.
6. We use the principle of moments to determine the . . . . .s at the supports of simply supported beams.
8. An application of a moment of a force is the use of a spanner to . . . . a nut.
9. Find the resultant of two forces of 3 N and 4 N at right angles to one another acting at a point. (Omit the first letter from the result to fit the clue into the crossword.)
12. The following forces act at a point: 6 N, $\underline{0°}$; 12 N, $\underline{90°}$; 4 N, $\underline{270°}$. Determine the magnitude of the resultant force.
13. This chapter
15. The following forces act at a point: 10 N, 90°; 8 N, 270°. State the magnitude of the resultant force.
17. An abbreviation for anticlockwise moment
18. Same as 17 down without a moment
19. The beginning and end of the quantity measured in newtons

13. Complete the crossword puzzle of Fig. 1.31 using Chapter 1 for reference material.

Figure 1.31

Across

1. This quantity is measured in newtons.
6. Any force $\underline{180°}$ less the two last letters
8. Used when drawing vector diagrams
9. Unit of force
11. Unit of length or distance
12. Part of a newton or opposite to off
13. Sent out when you are desperate for answers
15. Same as 12 across
16. Determine the force needed to move a wheel if its moment of force is 5.6 N m and the distance of the force from the centre of the wheel is 0.8 m.
18. If a beam is unstable it is likely to move . . or down.
20. Used in the calculation for centre of gravity
21. D.rectio.
22. Find the centre of gravity (*G*) of the thin sheet shown in Fig. 1.32. To solve the clue, round up the result to a whole number.

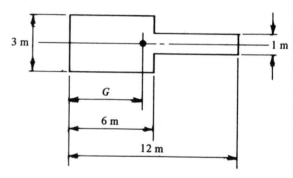

Figure 1.32

Down

2. This chapter
3. . . . . . . of gravity
4. Determine the moment of a force when a force of 0.5 N is acting at the end of a beam 4 m long.
5. When a body is displaced and it moves further away from its original position it is said to be . . . . (to solve the clue the word is in reverse).
7. Positions of stable equilibrium are positions of minimum potential . . . . . .

10. Important in the calculation of the centre of gravity
11. The centre of . . . . is the point at which the . . . . of a body is considered to be concentrated.
12. Same as 12 across
14. The reverse of the answer to 23 across
15. Same as 12 down
17. Determine the moment of a force when a force of 5 N is acting at the end of a beam 2 m long.
19. 3.142
20. Area with something missing

6. 0.2 m
7. 1.3 m
8. 15 N
9. 1.39 m
10. 40 N
11. 3.125 m
12. (a) 30 N, 10 N;
    (b) 28.33 N, 21.66 N;
    (c) 4.857 N, 7.143 N
13. 70 cm from A
14. (b) (i) 1.15 N m; (ii) 329 mm from B
15. 2 m from 8 N pulley
16. (b) 18.55 N up, 1.55 N down
17. 15 N, 136.7 mm from 5 N
18. 25 N
19. 22.5 N
20. 400 N, 600 N, extra 200 N on each

Answers

Section 1.4
4. 11.4 N, $\underline{22.5°}$
5. 18.0 N, $\underline{56.5°}$
6. 9.47 N, $\underline{126°}$
7. 85°
8. 5.70 N, $\underline{183°}$
9. 25.5 N, $\underline{270°}$
10. 70.0 N, $\underline{22°}$
11. 32.0 N, $\underline{68°}$
12. 183 N, $\underline{46°}$

Section 1.8
2. 50 N m
3. 24 N m
4. 15 N
5. 66.7 N

Section 1.11
1. 54.14 mm, 29.14 mm
2. (b) 75 mm, 50 mm
3. (b) 48.21 mm, 23.21 mm
4. Drawing
5. 107 mm from OA,
   94.6 mm from OB
6. 77.3 mm
7. 47.62 mm, 82.62 mm
8. (b) 41.67 mm
9. 102.3 mm from 175-mm side,
   70.5 mm from base
10. 115.5 mm from base
11. 66.67 mm, 100 mm

2 Pressure in fluids

2.1 SI units – symbols and abbreviations

Quantity	Symbol	Unit	Unit abbreviation
Acceleration due to gravity	g	metre per second squared	m/s²
Area	a	square metre	m²
Density	ρ	kilogram per cubic metre	kg/m³
Force	F	newton	N
Height	h	metre	m
Mass	m	kilogram	kg
Pressure	p	pascal	Pa
		bar	bar
		atmosphere	atm
Volume	V	cubic metre	m³

2.2 Definition of pressure

Pressure is defined as the force per unit area acting on the surface of a fluid, a fluid being a liquid or a gas:

$$\text{Pressure} = \frac{\text{force}}{\text{area}}$$

$$p = \frac{F}{a}$$

The unit of pressure is the pascal (Pa) and is equal to 1 N/m^2.

Examples

1. A force of 125 newtons is acting on an area of 0.5 square metres. Find the pressure acting on the surface.

$$F = 125 \text{ N}$$
$$a = 0.5 \text{ m}^2$$

$$\text{Pressure} = \frac{\text{force}}{\text{area}}$$

$$p = \frac{F}{a}$$

$$= \frac{125}{0.5}$$
$$= 250 \text{ Pa}$$

The pressure acting on the surface is 250 pascals.

2. A rectangular storage tank has a base of length 4 metres and width 2 metres. If the pressure acting on the base of the tank is 15 kilonewtons per square metre, determine the force involved.

$$a = 4 \times 2 = 8 \text{ m}^2$$
$$p = 15 \text{ kN/m}^2 = 15 \times 10^3 \text{ N/m}^2$$

$$\text{Pressure} = \frac{\text{force}}{\text{area}}$$

$$p = \frac{F}{a}$$

Therefore

$$F = ap$$
$$= 8 \times 15 \times 10^3$$
$$= 120 \times 10^3 \text{ N}$$
$$= 120 \text{ kN}$$

The force acting on the base of the tank is 120 kilonewtons.

3. Steam at a pressure of 3000 newtons per square metre is being applied to a piston, using a force of 40 kilonewtons. Determine the cross-sectional area of the piston.

$$p = 3000 \text{ N/m}^2$$
$$F = 40 \text{ kN} = 40 \times 10^3 \text{ N}$$

$$\text{Pressure} = \frac{\text{force}}{\text{area}}$$

$$p = \frac{F}{a}$$

Therefore

$$a = \frac{F}{p}$$

$$= \frac{40 \times 10^3}{3000}$$

$$= \frac{40}{3}$$

$$= 13.33 \text{ m}^2$$

The cross-sectional area of the piston is 13.33 square metres.

2.3 Pressure due to a column of liquid

Consider a column of liquid of cross-sectional area a and height h:

Volume of liquid = cross-sectional area × height
$$V = ah$$

From density $= \dfrac{\text{mass}}{\text{volume}}$

Mass = density × volume
$$m = \rho V$$
so $\qquad m = \rho ah$

Now force = mass × acceleration due to gravity

$$F = mg$$
so $\qquad F = \rho ahg$

But pressure $= \dfrac{\text{force}}{\text{area}}$

$$p = \frac{F}{a}$$

so $\qquad p = \dfrac{\rho ahg}{a}$

$$p = \rho hg$$

Examples
1. Calculate the pressure in a fluid at a depth of 150 millimetres if the density of the fluid is 14×10^3 kilograms per cubic metre, assuming the acceleration due to gravity is 9.8 metres per second squared.

$h = 150 \text{ mm} = 0.15 \text{ m}$
$\rho = 14 \times 10^3 \text{ kg/m}^3$
$g = 9.8 \text{ m/s}^2$

Pressure = density × depth
$\qquad\qquad$ × acceleration due to gravity
$$p = \rho h g$$
$$= 14 \times 10^3 \times 0.15 \times 9.8$$
$$= 20\,580 \text{ Pa}$$

The pressure in the fluid is 20 580 pascals.

2. A deep-sea diving vessel is designed to withstand pressures up to 100 meganewtons. Determine the safe maximum depth to which the vessel could descend if the density of sea water is 1100 kilograms per cubic metre and the acceleration due to gravity is 9.8 metres per second squared.

$p = 100 \text{ MN} = 100 \times 10^6 \text{ N}$
$\rho = 1100 \text{ kg/m}^3$
$g = 9.8 \text{ m/s}^2$

$$\text{Pressure} = \rho g h$$

so $\qquad h = \dfrac{p}{\rho g}$

$$= \frac{100 \times 10^6}{1100 \times 9.8}$$

$$= 9276 \text{ m}$$

The safe maximum depth is 9276 metres.

2.4 Direction of liquid pressure

A liquid under the force of gravity takes the shape of the container and finds its own level, as shown in Fig. 2.1. When the plunger is pushed down, pressure is exerted on the liquid which shoots out of the tiny holes in the vessel, as shown in Fig. 2.2. The pressure is acting in a direction normal (i.e., perpendicular) to the surface containing the liquid.

Figure 2.1

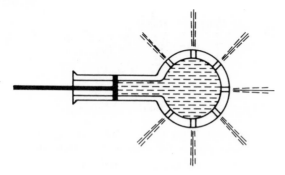

Figure 2.2

2.5 Atmospheric pressure

The pressure of the air upon us is called atmospheric pressure and is defined as the pressure that will support a column of mercury 760 millimetres high at 0 degrees Celsius at sea level and latitude 45°. One standard atmospheric pressure is 101 325 pascals, also known as 1 bar. The millibar (one-thousandth of a bar) is the unit of pressure used by meteorologists in weather forecasting. As shown in Sect. 2.3, pressure varies with depth; it also varies with height, an effect noticeable when mountain climbing. The pressure at the top of Mount Everest, the highest mountain in the world, is about 30% of that at sea level.

2.6 Absolute and gauge pressure

Absolute pressure is the pressure measured with respect to zero pressure, whereas gauge pressure is the pressure as measured by a gauge, i.e., that in excess of the pressure of the atmosphere. Therefore

Absolute pressure = gauge pressure
+ atmospheric pressure

2.7 Measurement of gas pressure

(a) The gas pressure, as shown in Fig. 2.3, is greater than the atmospheric pressure:

Gas pressure = atmospheric pressure
+ pressure due to a liquid column
of height h

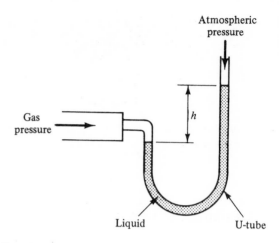

Figure 2.3

(b) The gas pressure, as shown in Fig. 2.4, is less than the atmospheric pressure:

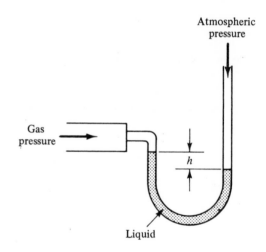

Figure 2.4

Gas pressure = atmospheric pressure
− pressure due to a liquid column
of height h

(c) Primary gauges include the liquid column manometer as shown in sections (a) and (b) but a more accurate measurement of pressure is taken by using a Bourdon gauge, shown in Fig. 2.5.

The Bourdon gauge consists of a curved tube of oval cross-section having one end closed and one end open to the pressure being measured. If the volume

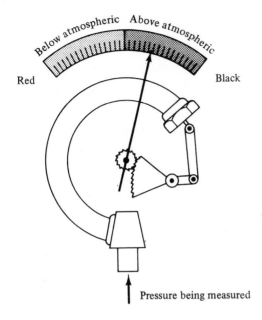

Red

Black

Pressure being measured

Figure 2.5

of the tube is made to increase by an excess of pressure the tube tends to straighten out. This movement is amplified and is shown as a pressure on a calibrated scale. This type of gauge is used to measure high pressures, as compared to the manometer which measures low pressures.

Example

1. A U-tube manometer containing mercury is connected to a gas cylinder. If the difference in height of the mercury is 0.8 metres, determine the gauge pressure and the absolute pressure if the density of mercury is 13.6 megagrammes per cubic metre, acceleration due to gravity is 9.8 metres per second squared, and atmospheric pressure is 101 325 pascals.

$h = 0.8$ m
$\rho = 13.6$ Mg/m^3 $= 13.6 \times 10^3$ kg/m^3
$g = 9.8$ m/s^2

Gauge pressure $p = \rho h g$
$\qquad\qquad\quad = 13.6 \times 10^3 \times 0.8 \times 9.8$
$\qquad\qquad\quad = 106\,624$ Pa

Absolute pressure = gauge pressure
$\qquad\qquad\qquad\quad$ + atmospheric pressure
$\qquad\qquad\qquad\; = 106\,624 + 101\,325$
$\qquad\qquad\qquad\; = 207\,949$ Pa

The gas gauge pressure is 106 624 pascals and the absolute pressure is 207 949 pascals or (approximately) the gauge pressure is 1.07 bars and the absolute pressure is 2.08 bars.

2.8 Exercise

1. Define the term 'pressure'.
2. Distinguish between the terms 'absolute' and 'gauge' pressures.
3. Explain with the aid of a sketch why the pressure at a given level in a fluid at rest is equal in all directions.
4. Explain with the aid of a sketch how the pressure acts in a direction normal to the surface containing the liquid.
5. Name three units of pressure.
6. A force of 250 N is distributed over an area of 0.8 m^2. Calculate the applied pressure.
7. The pressure in the fluid of a piston system is 200 kPa. Determine the force that this pressure will produce against a surface area of 0.04 m^2.
8. Calculate the surface area of a fluid when an applied force of 500 N creates a pressure of 2.5 Pa.
9. Show that the pressure of a column of liquid is proportional to the density and height of the liquid.
10. What is the pressure on a fluid of density 13 600 kg/m^3 if the height of the column is 650 mm? Assume that the acceleration due to gravity is 9.8 m/s^2.
11. Calculate the water pressure on the base of a dam which is holding water back at a depth of 100 m. Assume that the density of water is 1000 kg/m^3 and the acceleration due to gravity is 9.8 m/s^2.
12. Describe, with the aid of labelled diagrams, how gas pressure can be measured using: (a) a U-tube manometer and (b) a pressure gauge.
13. Calculate the gauge pressure for a U-tube manometer when the difference in height reading is 140 mm. Take the acceleration due to gravity as 9.8 m/s^2 and the density of the U-tube liquid as 13 × 10^3 kg/m^3.
14. If atmospheric pressure is 101 325 Pa, what is absolute pressure when the gauge pressure is 100 000 Pa?

15. Explain, with the aid of a labelled sketch, the action and construction of a pressure gauge.
16. Complete the crossword puzzle of Fig. 2.6 using Chapter 2 for reference material.

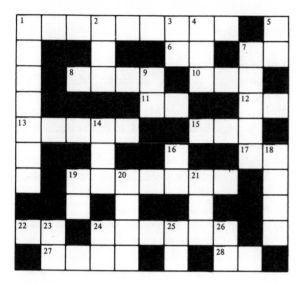

Figure 2.6

Across
1. Measures low pressure
6. Kilonewt.
7. Abbreviation for milligram
8. Absolute pressure is the gauge pressure measured with respect to . . . . pressure.
10. See Sect. 2.3. Pressure . . . to a column of liquid
11. Opposite to yes
12. See Sect. 2.2, Example 3 – pis . . n
13. Drawn in Fig. 2.3
15. Unit of pressure
17. Type of water without the first letter
19. 9.81 m/s^2 is acceleration due to . . . .
22. Megapascal, almost
24. Unit of force
27. Pressure is defined as force per unit . . . .
28. Opposite to off

Down
1. Atmospheric pressure is defined as the pressure that will support a column of . . . . 760 mm high at 0°C at sea level.

2. Calculate the force when a pressure of 20 N/m^2 is acting on an area of 0.05 m^2.
3. Accelera.i.n
4. Not the beginning
5. Abbreviated unit of mass
7. Unit of length
9. See 28 across.
14. One standard atmospheric pressure equals one . . .
16. A system of units
18. Square measure
19. Kilogram abbreviated in reverse
20. Same as 18 down
21. A force of 0.5 N is distributed over an area of 0.25 m^2. Determine the pressure.
23. Abbreviated unit of pressure
25. Me.e.rologist
26. . . rmal

17. Complete the crossword puzzle of Fig. 2.7 using Chapter 2 for reference material.

Figure 2.7

Across
1. Type of pressure
4. Mass per unit volume
6. The atmosphere
8. Bourdon . . . . .
9. Abbreviated pascal

10. Unit is the newton
12. Abbreviated unit of mass
13. Often contains mercury

Down
  1. Pressure = force/ ?
  2. Unit of length
  3. Force per unit area
  5. $p = \rho h$?, but in reverse
  7. Part of a pressure formula
  10. . orce of grav. .y
  11. Unit of pressure — reversed

Answers

Section 2.8
  6. 312.5 Pa
  7. 8 kN
  8. 200 m^2
  9. Proof
  10. 86.6 kPa
  11. 98 kPa
  13. 17.8 kPa
  14. 201.3 kPa

3 Elasticity of materials

3.1 SI units — symbols and abbreviations

Quantity	Symbol	Unit	Unit abbreviation
Area	a	square metre	m²
Force	F	newton	N
Length	l	metre	m
Strain		—	
Stress		newton per square metre	N/m²
Young's modulus	E	newton per square metre	N/m²

3.2 Tension, compression, and shear

A material is said to be under tension when it is being pulled apart as shown in Fig. 3.1.

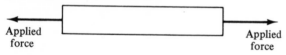

Applied force   Applied force

Figure 3.1

A material is said to be under compression when it is being squashed as shown in Fig. 3.2.

Applied force   Applied force

Figure 3.2

A material, i.e. the rivet, is said to be in shear when it is subjected to forces as shown in Fig. 3.3.

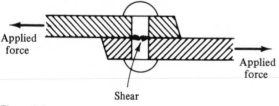

Applied force   Applied force

Shear

Figure 3.3

3.3 Force and extension 📼

When materials are subjected to force they change their shape. If the force is within the elastic limit the material will return to its original shape when the force is removed. A graph of a material showing force against extension can be seen in Fig. 3.4. The amount

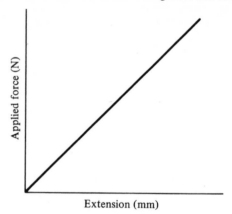

Figure 3.4

of extension of a material is found by applying Hooke's law, which states that, within the elastic limit, the extension of a material is directly proportional to the applied force. Therefore:

$$\text{Extension} \propto \text{applied force}$$
$$\text{Extension} = \text{constant} \times \text{applied force}$$
$$\text{so} \qquad \text{constant} = \frac{\text{extension}}{\text{applied force}}$$

Example

1. The following results were obtained when a length of wire was subjected to gradually increasing forces.

Tensile force (newtons)	0	5	10	15	20	25	30
Extension (millimetres)	0	0.02	0.04	0.06	0.08	0.10	0.12

Plot a graph of tensile force against extension and from it determine: (a) the tensile force which produces an extension in the wire of 0.03 millimetres and (b) the extension produced by a force of 23 newtons.

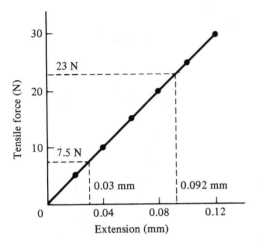

Figure 3.5

From the graph of Fig. 3.5 it can be seen that (a) a force of 7.5 newtons produces an extension of 0.03 millimetres and (b) an extension of 0.092 millimetres is caused by a force of 23 newtons.

Note that in practice a perfectly straight line would not be obtained so from experimental results the best straight line would need to be drawn.

3.4 Stress

The stress in a material is defined as the force per unit area:

$$\text{Stress} = \frac{\text{applied force}}{\text{cross-sectional area}}$$

$$= \frac{F}{a}$$

Example
1. Calculate the stress in a bar of cross-sectional area 50 square millimetres when subjected to a force of 400 newtons.

$F = 400 \text{ N}$
$a = 50 \text{ mm}^2 = 50 \times 10^{-6} \text{ m}^2$

$$\text{Stress} = \frac{\text{applied force}}{\text{cross-sectional area}}$$

$$= \frac{F}{a}$$

$$= \frac{400}{50 \times 10^{-6}}$$

$$= \frac{400 \times 10^6}{50}$$

$$= 8 \times 10^6 \text{ N/m}^2$$

$$= 8 \text{ MN/m}^2$$

The stress in the bar is 8 meganewtons per square metre.

3.5 Strain 📼

When a force is applied to a material it can be distorted, or strained. Strain is the ratio of change of length in a material to its original length:

$$\text{Strain} = \frac{\text{change in length}}{\text{original length}}$$

$$= \frac{\Delta l}{l}$$

Strain has no units because it is a ratio of lengths.

Example
1. An extension of 0.2 millimetres takes place in a 4-metre rod when subjected to an applied force. Calculate the strain produced in the rod.

$\Delta l = 0.2 \text{ mm} = 0.2 \times 10^{-3} \text{ m}$
$l = 4 \text{ m}$

$$\text{Strain} = \frac{\text{change in length}}{\text{original length}}$$

$$= \frac{\Delta l}{l}$$

$$= \frac{0.2 \times 10^{-3}}{4}$$

$$= \frac{0.2}{4 \times 10^3}$$

$$= \frac{0.05}{10^3}$$

$$= 0.000\,05$$

The strain produced in the rod is 0.000 05.

3.6 Young's modulus or modulus of elasticity 📼

Within the elastic limit of a material, stress is proportional to strain:

$$\text{Stress} \propto \text{strain}$$
$$\text{Stress} = \text{strain} \times \text{constant}$$

Therefore $\quad \text{constant} = \dfrac{\text{stress}}{\text{strain}}$

This constant is known as Young's modulus or the modulus of elasticity:

$$\text{Modulus of elasticity} = \frac{\text{stress}}{\text{strain}}$$

$$E = \frac{\text{stress}}{\text{strain}}$$

Examples

1. Calculate the modulus of elasticity of a bar if a stress of 5000 newtons per square metre results in a strain of 0.000 02.

Stress = 5000 N/m²
Strain = 0.000 02

$$\text{Modulus of elasticity} = \frac{\text{stress}}{\text{strain}}$$

$$E = \frac{\text{stress}}{\text{strain}}$$

$$= \frac{5000}{0.000\,02}$$

$$= 250\,000\,000 \text{ N/m}^2$$

$$= 250 \text{ MN/m}^2$$

The modulus of elasticity of the bar is 250 meganewtons per square metre.

2. A tie bar has a cross-sectional area of 100 square millimetres and carries a load of 40 000 newtons. Under this load its length increases by 1.5 millimetres over an initial length of 2 metres. Calculate: (a) the stress in the bar, (b) the strain in the bar, and (c) the modulus of elasticity.

$F = 40\,000$ N
$a = 100$ mm² $= 100 \times 10^{-6}$ m²
$\Delta l = 1.5$ mm $= 1.5 \times 10^{-3}$ m
$l = 2$ m

$$\text{Stress} = \frac{\text{applied force}}{\text{cross-sectional area}}$$

$$= \frac{F}{a} = \frac{40\,000}{100 \times 10^{-6}} = 400 \times 10^6 \text{ N/m}^2$$

$$\text{Strain} = \frac{\text{change in length}}{\text{original length}}$$

$$= \frac{\Delta l}{l} = \frac{1.5 \times 10^{-3}}{2} = 0.75 \times 10^{-3}$$

$$= 0.000\,75$$

$$\begin{array}{l}\text{Modulus of} \\ \text{elasticity}\end{array} = \frac{\text{stress}}{\text{strain}} = \frac{400 \times 10^6}{0.000\,75}$$

$$= 533\,333 \times 10^6 \text{ N/m}^2$$

The stress in the bar is 400 meganewtons per square metre with a strain of 0.000 75 with a modulus of elasticity of 533 333 meganewtons per square metre.

3.7 Exercise

1. A steel bolt of cross-sectional area 150 mm² is subjected to an applied force of 40 kN. Calculate the stress in the bolt.
2. If the stress on a rod of 100 mm² is not to exceed 24 MN/m² calculate the applied force.
3. A tie bar 1 m long has a cross-sectional area of 200 mm² and carries a load of 32 kN. Under this load the tie bar increases its length by 0.5 mm. Calculate the stress and strain in the bar.
4. A load of 50 kN produces an extension of 4 mm in a metal rod of cross-sectional area 200 mm² and length 2 m. Calculate the stress, strain, and the value of Young's modulus for the metal.

5. Draw a load extension graph from the following data:

Load (N)	400	800	1200	1600	2000	2400
Extension (mm)	0.25	0.50	0.75	1.00	1.25	1.50

From the graph determine the extension produced by a load of 1500 N.

6. A test on a steel wire gave the following results:

Applied force (N)	0	50	100	150	200	250	300
Extension (mm)	0	0.2	0.4	0.6	0.75	0.95	1.15

Draw a graph and show the approximate elastic limit point. Using the part of the graph that obeys Hooke's law, determine:
(a) the applied force necessary to produce an extension of 0.3 mm,
(b) the extension produced by an applied force of 120 N.

7. (a) State and define the SI unit of force.
(b) If a force of 150 N produces an elastic extension of 6 mm in a steel wire, calculate the extension produced by 80 N.   (EMFEC)

8. (a) Draw diagrams to show the difference between tensile, compressive and shear forces.
(b) State Hooke's law.
(c) A piece of material is subjected to a tensile force of 600 kN and extends 0.05 mm. Calculate the extension if the force is increased by 3 MN, assuming Hooke's law is obeyed.   (EMFEC)

9. The following table refers to an experiment to determine the relationship between load and extension for a steel wire 1 mm in diameter and 1.2 m long:

Load (N)	0	5	10	15	20	25	30
Extension (mm)	0	0.25	0.5	0.8	1.0	1.25	1.45

Plot a graph of load against extension and hence determine the value of Young's modulus for the steel.   (WJEC)

10. The following results were obtained from a tensile test on an iron wire 0.7 mm in diameter and 2.3 m long:

Load (N)	0	2	4	6	8	10	12
Extension (mm)	0	0.25	0.48	0.75	1.0	1.3	1.5

Draw a graph of load against extension for the wire and from it determine the value of Young's modulus. In such a test, how would you verify that the material does not exceed the elastic limit during loading?   (EMFEC)

11. Define: (a) a tensile force and (b) a compressive force applied to a material.
   An extension of 0.4 mm occurred in a 3-m rod when subjected to a load. Calculate the strain produced in the rod.   (YHCFE)

12. Name the three different kinds of stress and describe them with the aid of sketches.
   A mild steel bar, 6 mm in diameter, carries a load of 100 N. Calculate the stress.   (WMAC)

13. A bar of steel is 44 mm in diameter and 6 m long. Under a tensile load of 12 kN the length is increased by 2.25 mm. Determine: (a) the strain and (b) the stress produced.

14. A steel wire 6 m long and 2 mm in diameter is found to extend by 4 mm when a tensile load of 35 N is applied. Calculate the stress and the strain in the wire.   (EMFEC)

15. (a) Explain what is meant by 'an elastic material'.
(b) A test on a specimen of mild steel of rectangular cross-section area 0.002 m² gave an extension of 0.08 mm on a 200-mm gauge length due to a load of 15 kN. Calculate the stress and the strain. If a 4-m bar of the same section is subjected to a tensile load of 9 kN what will be the extension?   (EMFEC)

16. Explain what is meant by the term 'stress'.
   The diameter of a steam engine cylinder is 225 mm. The cylinder cover is held in position by six bolts, each having an effective diameter of 20 mm. If the pressure of the steam in the cylinder is 0.1 N/mm² calculate the stress in each bolt, assuming that the bolts carry the total thrust due to the steam pressure.   (EMFEC)

17. The application of force to a solid material may set up stresses of three simple types. State the

type of stress which occurs in the following four examples:
(a) the legs of a table which is loaded with books,
(b) the pin joining two links of a cycle chain,
(c) the cord by which a picture hangs from its hook,
(d) the tightened cylinder-head studs of a petrol engine. (WJEC)

18. (a) A nut is screwed up tightly on a bolt holding together two machine pieces. Describe, with the aid of sketches, the kind of stress occurring in: (i) the shank of the bolt, (ii) the machine pieces, (iii) the threads of the bolt.
(b) What force prevents the nut from unscrewing?
(c) If the bolt shank is 6 mm in diameter and the nut exerts a tightening force of 250 N, calculate the stress in the shank ($\pi = 3\frac{1}{7}$). (WMAC)

19. A stud for a lifting device is shown in Fig. 3.6. A load W is applied at the lower end, the upper end of the stud being fixed into the machine frame.

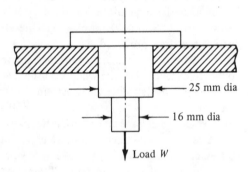

25 mm dia

16 mm dia

Load W

Figure 3.6

(a) Find the stress in the 16-mm diameter portion of the stud if the load W is 2 kN.
(b) Find the load W if the stress in the 25-mm diameter portion is not to exceed 8 N/mm^2.
(c) What type of stress is in the 16-mm and 25-mm diameter portions? (NCFE)

20. A tie bar having a 25-mm square section is 2 m long. When carrying a load of 4 kN its extension is 0.5 mm. Another tie bar of 20-mm square section and of the same material has a length of 1 m and carries a load of 2.5 kN. What will be the extension of this second tie bar? (WMAC)

21. (a) Explain the meaning of the terms 'proportional law' and 'elastic limit load' as applied to the strength of materials.
(b) Calculate the necessary minimum diameter of a rod which is required to sustain a direct pull of 15 kN if the stress is not to exceed 13 N/mm^2. Calculate also the strain due to the given load if the rod is 4 m long and the extension is 2 mm. (EMFEC)

22. Complete the crossword puzzle of Fig. 3.7 using Chapter 3 as reference material.

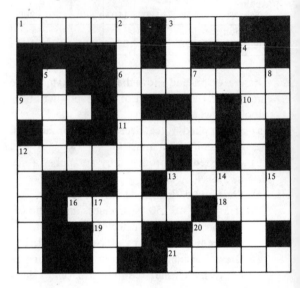

Figure 3.7

Across
1. When materials are subjected to . . . . . they change their shape.
3. Calculate the force (MN) on a rod of cross-sectional area 0.4 mm^2 if the stress is 25 MN/mm^2.
6. The state of a material when it is being pulled apart
9. If a force of 100 N produces an elastic extension of 0.5 mm, calculate the extension produced by 200 N.
10. Unit abbreviation for millimetre
11. Calculate the stress (MN/mm^2) in a bar of cross-sectional area 50 mm^2 where subjected to a force of 450 N.
12. Force per unit area

13. Unit of length in reverse
16. A law? Within the elastic limit, the extension of a material is directly proportional to the applied force.
18. Stress = applied force/ ?
19. Not out
21. Hooke had one in his law.

Down

2. Strain = ?/original length
3. Calculate the modulus of elasticity (MN/m^2) of a bar of material if a stress of 500 N/m^2 results in a strain of 0.000 05.
4. The state of a material when it is being squashed but without the last two letters
5. There is an SI system in this word.
7. A rivet is often subjected to this type of force.
8. An abbreviated meganewton but in reverse
12. Change in length/original length — omit the last letter.
13. A well-known word with letters missing — .xt.nsion
14. The first letter of tension and compression
15. This chapter is about elasticity of . .terials
17. Slipped into this chapter
20. A system of units

Answers

Section 3.7
1. 267 MN/m^2
2. 2400 N
3. 160 MN/m^2, 0.000 5
4. 250 MN/m^2, 0.002, 125 000 MN/m^2
5. 0.937 5 mm
6. (a) 75 N; (b) 0.48 mm
7. (b) 3.2 mm
8. (c) 0.25 mm
9. 30 554 N/mm^2
10. 47 805 N/mm^2
11. 0.000 133 3
12. 3.536 N/mm^2
13. (a) 0.000 375; (b) 0.789 N/mm^2
14. 11.14 N/mm^2, 0.000 333 3
15. (b) 7.5 MN/m^2, 0.000 4
16. 0.009 375 N/mm^2
18. (c) 8.842 N/mm^2
19. (a) 9.946 N/mm^2; (b) 3927.5 N
20. 0.2441 mm
21. (b) 38.33 mm, 0.0005

4 Motion

4.1 SI units — symbols and abbreviations

Quantity	Symbol	Unit	Unit abbreviation
Acceleration	a	metre per second squared	m/s²
Acceleration due to gravity	g	metre per second squared	m/s²
Distance	s	metre	m
Force	F	newton	N
Frequency	f	hertz	Hz
Mass	m	kilogram	kg
Time	t	second	s
Velocity, initial	u	metre per second	m/s
Velocity, final	v	metre per second	m/s
Wavelength	λ	metre	m
Work	W	newton metre	N m

4.2 Speed 📼

Speed is defined as the rate at which distance is covered without taking direction into account:

$$\text{Average speed } (v) = \frac{\text{total distance covered } (s)}{\text{time } (t)}$$

From $v = \dfrac{s}{t}$ we get $s = vt$ and $t = \dfrac{s}{v}$.

Example

1. A motorist covers the distance from London to Newcastle-on-Tyne, a distance of 450 kilometres, in 6 hours. Calculate the average speed in kilometres per hour and metres per second.

$s = 450$ km

$t = 6$ h

$$\text{Average speed } (v) = \frac{s}{t} = \frac{450}{6} = 75 \text{ km/h}$$

or

$$s = 450 \times 1000 = 450\,000 \text{ m}$$

and $\qquad t = 6 \times 60 \times 60 = 21\,600$ s

$$\text{Average speed } (v) = \frac{s}{t} = \frac{450\,000}{21\,600} = 20.83 \text{ m/s}$$

The average speed is 75 kilometres per hour or 20.83 metres per second.

4.3 Velocity and acceleration

Velocity is defined as the rate at which distance is covered and takes direction into account:

$$\text{Velocity } (v) = \frac{\text{distance travelled in a defined direction } (s)}{\text{time } (t)}$$

Acceleration is defined as the rate of change of velocity. Let u = initial velocity and v = final velocity; then change of velocity = $v - u$ so:

$$\text{Acceleration } (a) = \text{rate of change of velocity}$$

$$= \frac{v - u}{t}$$

From $a = \dfrac{v - u}{t}$ we get $v = u + at$

and

$$u = v - at \quad \text{and} \quad t = \frac{v - u}{a}.$$

Example

1. A vehicle starting from rest reaches a velocity of 40 metres per second travelling north, in 10 seconds. Determine the rate of acceleration, assuming it to be uniform.

$u = 0$

$v = 40$ m/s

$t = 10$ s

$$\text{Acceleration } (a) = \frac{v - u}{t} = \frac{40 - 0}{10} = \frac{40}{10} = 4 \text{ m/s}^2$$

The rate of acceleration is 4 metres per second squared.

4.4 Distance

To calculate the distance travelled by a body during a uniform acceleration from velocity u to velocity v, we can assume the average velocity to be halfway between u and v.

Average velocity $= \dfrac{u + v}{2}$

Distance (s) = average velocity × time

$$= \dfrac{u + v}{2} \times t$$

$$= \tfrac{1}{2}t(u + v)$$

Example

1. A body with a velocity of 20 metres per second accelerates at 5 metres per second for 15 seconds. Calculate the final velocity and the distance travelled.

$u = 20$ m/s
$a = 5$ m/s^2
$t = 15$ s

Final velocity $(v) = u + at = 20 + (5 \times 15)$
$\qquad\qquad\qquad = 20 + 75 = 95$ m/s

Distance $(s) = \tfrac{1}{2}t(u + v) = \tfrac{1}{2} \times 15(20 + 95)$
$\qquad\qquad = \tfrac{1}{2} \times 15 \times 115 = 862.5$ m

The final velocity is 95 metres per second with a distance travelled of 862.5 metres.

4.5 Equations of motion

From Sect. 4.3 we have $v = u + at$ and from Sect. 4.4, $s = \tfrac{1}{2}t(u + v)$. With this information we can derive two other equations:

Substitute $v = u + at$ into $s = \tfrac{1}{2}t(u + v)$; we get
$$s = \tfrac{1}{2}t(u + u + at)$$
$$s = \tfrac{1}{2}t(2u + at)$$
$$s = ut + \tfrac{1}{2}at^2$$

Also, from $s = \tfrac{1}{2}t(u + v)$ we get $t = \dfrac{2s}{u + v}$.

Substitute $t = \dfrac{2s}{u + v}$ into $v = u + at$; we get

$$v = u + \dfrac{2s}{u + v}$$

$$v - u = \dfrac{2as}{u + v}$$

$$(v - u)(v + u) = 2as$$

$$v^2 - u^2 = 2as$$

$$v^2 = u^2 + 2as$$

Summary: $\quad v = u + at$
$\qquad\qquad s = \tfrac{1}{2}t(u + v)$
$\qquad\qquad s = ut + \tfrac{1}{2}at^2$
$\qquad\qquad v^2 = u^2 + 2as$

Examples

1. Calculate the distance travelled by a train in 50 seconds if its velocity in a particular direction is 20 metres per second but accelerating at 0.5 metres per second squared.

$u = 20$ m/s
$a = 0.5$ m/s^2
$t = 50$ s

Distance $(s) = ut + \tfrac{1}{2}at^2 = (20 \times 50) + (\tfrac{1}{2} \times 0.5 \times 50^2)$
$\qquad\qquad = 1000 + 625 = 1625$ m

The distance travelled is 1625 metres.

2. A car accelerates from rest at the rate of 2 metres per second squared during a period of 5 seconds. Determine the distance travelled during acceleration.

$u = 0$
$a = 2$ m/s^2
$t = 5$ s

Distance $(s) = ut + \tfrac{1}{2}at^2 = (0 \times 5) + (\tfrac{1}{2} \times 2 \times 5^2)$
$\qquad\qquad = 0 + 25 = 25$ m

The distance travelled during acceleration is 25 metres.

3. A vehicle starts from rest and accelerates at a rate of 2 metres per second squared for a distance of 2000 metres. Calculate the final velocity.

$a = 2 \text{ m/s}^2$
$u = 0$
$s = 2000 \text{ m}$

Final velocity $v^2 = u^2 + 2as = 0 + (2 \times 2 \times 2000)$
$$= 8000$$

Therefore $\qquad v = \sqrt{8000} = 89.4 \text{ m/s}$

The final velocity is 89.4 metres per second.

4.6 Acceleration due to gravity

When objects fall freely their acceleration is at a fixed rate of $g = 9.81$ metres per second squared. To solve problems involving the force of gravity the equations of motion are modified; acceleration (a) is replaced by the acceleration due to gravity (g).

Examples

1. A stone is dropped from a tower and falls freely from rest. Calculate the distance the stone falls after 5 seconds, assuming the acceleration due to gravity is 9.81 metres per second squared.

$t = 5 \text{ s}$
$g = 9.81 \text{ m/s}^2$

Distance (s) $= ut + \frac{1}{2}gt^2 = (0 \times 5) + (\frac{1}{2} \times 9.81 \times 5^2)$
$$= 0 + 122.6 = 122.6 \text{ m}$$

The stone falls through a distance of 122.6 metres.

2. A body is dropped from a tower with zero initial velocity and a final velocity of 50 metres per second. Calculate the height of the tower if the time of the fall is 4 seconds.

$v = 50 \text{ m/s}$
$u = 0$
$t = 4 \text{ s}$
$g = 9.81 \text{ m/s}^2$

From $v^2 = u^2 + 2gs$ we get

$$s = \frac{v^2 - u^2}{2g} = \frac{50^2 + 0}{2 \times 9.81} = \frac{2500}{19.62} = 127.4 \text{ m}$$

The height of the tower is 127.4 metres.

4.7 Exercise

1. Define the terms 'speed', 'velocity', 'acceleration', and 'acceleration due to gravity'.
2. State the units of speed, velocity, and acceleration.
3. Explain the difference between speed and velocity.
4. A body is accelerated from zero velocity to a velocity of 8 m/s in a time of 2 s. Calculate the acceleration.
5. A car accelerates from 16 m/s to 34 m/s in 8 s. Calculate the acceleration.
6. An aeroplane on take off accelerates from zero velocity to 30 m/s with an average acceleration of 2 m/s². Calculate:
   (a) the time taken and (b) the distance covered.
7. A car moves from rest with an acceleration of 3 m/s². Determine the velocity of the car after a time of 20 s.
8. A stone is dropped from a bridge. Calculate the distance the stone falls after 8 s, assuming the acceleration due to gravity is 9.81 m/s².
9. A train accelerates from rest at a rate of 0.6 m/s². Find the time taken and the distance travelled when the speed has reached 60 km/h.
10. Starting from rest a car accelerates uniformly to a speed of 30 km/h in 20 s. Its speed then falls to 20 km/h. The brakes are then applied to bring the car to rest in 3 s. The total distance travelled is 6000 m. Find the distance it moves when accelerating and when braking, and the time taken for the whole journey.   (YHCFE)
11. A car at a given instant has a speed of 12 km/h. It is given a uniform retardation of 2.5 m/s² until its speed is reduced to 7 km/h. Determine the time taken in reducing the speed and the distance the car has travelled during retardation.
                                                (NWRAC)
12. An electric train starting from rest at one station comes to rest at the next station 7200 m away in 3.5 min, having first a uniform acceleration, then a uniform speed for 2.5 min, then a uniform retardation. The time of acceleration is twice the time of retardation. Find: (a) the uniform speed at which the train runs for 2.5 min, (b) the uniform acceleration, (c) the uniform retardation, (d) the space passed over, during the acceleration

period, and (e) the space passed over, during the time of retardation. (WMAC)

13. A vehicle starts from rest and its speed increases uniformly to 30 km/h in 15 s, then for some time remains steady at 30 km/h. Obtain: (a) the distance covered in the first minute, (b) the average velocity during the first 10 s, and (c) the average velocity during the first 418 m.

14. A train starts from rest and increases speed at a uniform rate to reach 60 km/h in 2 min. It then travels at this constant speed for 10 min, after which the speed is decreased at a uniform rate until the train comes to rest. The total distance travelled by the train is 13 km. Determine: (a) the time taken for the train to come to rest from maximum speed and (b) the average speed of the train. (NCFE)

15. A train starts from rest and reaches a speed of 45 km/h in 2 min, the rate of acceleration being uniform. The train then travels at a uniform speed of 45 km/h until a total distance of 6 km has been covered. Find: (a) the distance travelled by the train during the acceleration period, (b) the total time required to travel the 6 km, and (c) the average speed of the train. (NCFE)

16. An object is dropped from a building and takes 4 s to reach the ground. Calculate: (a) the height of the building and (b) the velocity with which it strikes the ground.

17. A ball is thrown vertically upwards with a velocity of 15 m/s. Determine: (a) the height reached and (b) the time taken.

18. Calculate the velocity at which an object hits the ground if it is dropped through a height of 200 m.

19. An object is thrown directly downwards with an initial velocity of 6 m/s and takes 5 s to reach the ground. Determine: (a) the height from which it was thrown and (b) the velocity on reaching the ground.

4.8 Distance–time graph 📼

The movement of a body can be represented pictorially by means of a graph as shown in Fig. 4.1. The gradient or slope of the graph represents the speed of the body and can be found as follows:

(a) Choose any two points on the straight line.

(b) Read the coordinates of each point.

(c) Calculate the difference between the two vertical points.

(d) Calculate the difference between the two horizontal points.

(e) Calculate the slope of the straight line using the formula:

$$\text{Slope} = \frac{\text{difference between the two vertical points}}{\text{difference between the two horizontal points}}$$

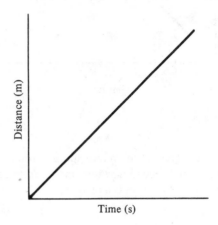

Figure 4.1

Example

1. A vehicle travels at a constant speed over a distance of 100 metres. The table shows the times recorded at various distances:

Time (seconds)	0	4	8	12	16	20
Distance (metres)	0	20	40	60	80	100

Draw the distance–time graph (Fig. 4.2) and from it determine: (a) the average speed of the vehicle and (b) the time taken to cover a distance of 30 metres.

From the graph:

$$\text{Vertical distance} = 90 - 40 = 50 \text{ m}$$
$$\text{Horizontal distance} = 18 - 8 = 10 \text{ s}$$
$$\text{Slope} = \frac{\text{vertical distance}}{\text{horizontal distance}}$$
$$\text{i.e., Speed} = \frac{50}{10} = 5 \text{ m/s}$$

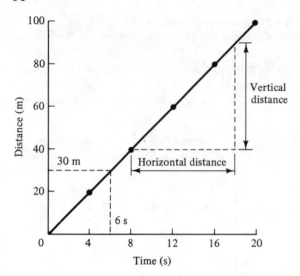

Figure 4.2

From the graph, the average speed is found to be 5 metres per second and the time taken to cover a distance of 30 metres is 6 seconds.

4.9 Velocity–time graph (acceleration) 🔲

The graph drawn in Fig. 4.3 represents a body whose velocity increases from zero to a final velocity of v metres per second in a time of t_1 seconds; the velocity is then constant until it reaches a time of t_2 seconds;

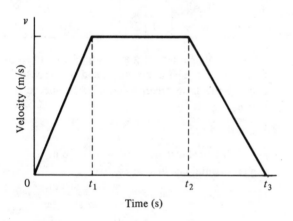

Figure 4.3

the body then slows down to zero velocity reaching a time of t_3 seconds. This slowing down process is termed deceleration or retardation, i.e., negative acceleration.

The slope of a velocity–time graph is the acceleration of the body.

Examples

1. The velocity of a motor car changes uniformly from 16 metres per second to 32 metres per second in 10 seconds. Draw a velocity–time graph (Fig. 4.4) and from it determine the rate of acceleration.

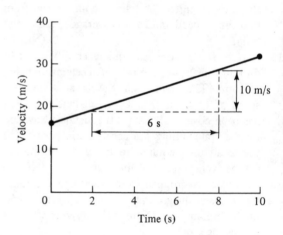

Figure 4.4

From the graph:

$$\text{Vertical distance} = 10 \text{ m/s}$$
$$\text{Horizontal distance} = 6 \text{ s}$$
$$\text{Slope} = \frac{\text{vertical distance}}{\text{horizontal distance}}$$
$$\text{i.e., acceleration} = \frac{10}{6} = 1.67 \text{ m/s}^2$$

The rate of acceleration is 1.67 metres per second squared.

2. A vehicle travelling at a velocity of 30 metres per second decelerates to a standstill in 15 seconds. Draw a velocity–time graph (Fig. 4.5) and from it determine the rate of deceleration.

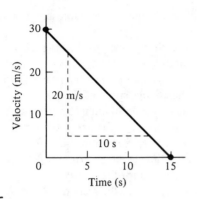

Figure 4.5

From the graph:

Vertical distance = – 20 m/s
Horizontal distance = 10 s

$$\text{Slope} = \frac{\text{vertical distance}}{\text{horizontal distance}}$$

$$\text{Deceleration} = \frac{-20}{10} = -2 \text{ m/s}^2$$

The negative sign indicates that the vehicle is decelerating. The rate of deceleration is 2 metres per second squared.

4.10 Velocity–time graph (distance)

The area under a velocity-time graph over a given interval of time represents the distance moved in the direction of that velocity in that time.

Examples
1. Calculate the distance moved by a body travelling at a constant velocity of 40 metres per second for 20 seconds. Use two methods of solution.

Graphical method (Fig. 4.6):

Distance moved = area under graph
= 40 m/s × 20 s
= 800 m

Formula method:

Distance (s) = velocity × time
= 40 m/s × 20 s
= 800 m

The distance moved by the body is 800 metres.

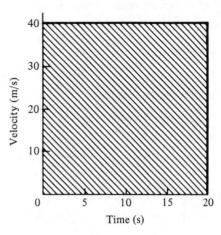

Figure 4.6

2. A body starts from rest and accelerates uniformly to a velocity of 20 metres per second covering a distance of 800 metres. It then travels at a constant velocity for the next 10 kilometres and is brought to rest with a uniform deceleration of 0.5 metres per second squared. Draw a velocity–time graph (Fig. 4.7) and from it determine: (a) the total time of the journey, (b) the total distance covered, and (c) the average velocity for the journey.

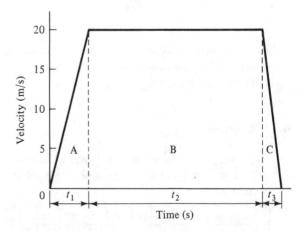

Figure 4.7

Consider uniform acceleration:

Distance travelled = area A

$$800 = \tfrac{1}{2} \times t_1 \times 20$$
$$800 = 10t_1$$
$$t_1 = \frac{800}{10} = 80 \text{ s}$$

Consider constant velocity:

Distance travelled = area B

$$10\,000 = t_2 \times 20$$
$$t_2 = \frac{10\,000}{20} = 500 \text{ s}$$

Consider deceleration:

Deceleration = slope of graph

$$0.5 = \frac{20 - 0}{t_3}$$
$$t_3 = \frac{20}{0.5} = 40 \text{ s}$$

Distance travelled = area C
$$= \tfrac{1}{2} \times 40 \times 20$$
$$= 400 \text{ m}$$

Total time $= 80 + 500 + 40$
$$= 620 \text{ s}$$

Total distance $= 800 + 10\,000 + 400$
$$= 11\,200 \text{ m}$$
$$= 11.2 \text{ km}$$

$$\text{Average velocity} = \frac{\text{total distance}}{\text{total time}}$$
$$= \frac{11\,200}{620}$$
$$= 18.07 \text{ m/s}$$

The time taken to cover a distance of 11.2 kilometres is 620 seconds with an average velocity of 18.07 metres per second.

4.11 Exercise

1. A car travels at a constant speed over a distance of 200 m. The table shows the times recorded at various distances:

Time (s)	0	10	20	30	40	50	60	70	80
Distance (m)	0	25	50	75	100	125	150	175	200

Draw a distance-time graph and from it determine:
   (a) the time taken to cover a distance of 40 metres,
   (b) the distance covered in a time of 75 seconds,
   (c) the average speed of the car.

2. A vehicle travels 90 km in 2 h at a constant speed and then travels a further 100 km in 1.5 h, again at constant speed. From this information plot a distance-time graph and from it determine:
   (a) the speed for the first 90 km,
   (b) the speed for the second 100 km,
   (c) the average speed for the total distance,
   (d) the distance travelled after 2.5 h,
   (e) the time taken to travel 170 km.

3. A vehicle travels a distance of 30 m in 3 s at a constant speed. It is then stationary for 2 s before moving a further 25 m in 3 s. Draw the distance-time graph and from it determine the average speed over the whole distance.

4. The velocity of a car changes uniformly from 20 m/s to 40 m/s in 8 s. Draw a velocity-time graph and from it determine the rate of acceleration.

5. A car travelling at a velocity of 40 m/s slows down to a standstill in 20 s. Draw a velocity-time graph and from it determine the rate of deceleration.

6. A train makes a journey between two stations in 10 min. The velocity of the train is given in the table:

Time (s)	0	100	200	300	400	500	600
Velocity (m/s)	0	4	7.4	11	14.5	14.5	0

Draw the velocity-time graph and from it determine:
   (a) the acceleration between 0 and 400 s,
   (b) the deceleration between 500 and 600 s.

7. Calculate the distance moved by a body travelling at a constant velocity of 50 m/s for 30 s. Use two methods of solution.

8. A vehicle starts from rest and accelerates smoothly to a velocity of 30 m/s covering a distance of 1 km. It then travels at constant velocity for the next 8 km and is brought to rest with uniform deceleration of 0.8 m/s². Draw a velocity-time graph and from it determine:

(a) the total time of the journey,
(b) the total distance covered,
(c) the average velocity for the journey.

9. A vehicle starts from rest with uniform acceleration for 35 s when its velocity is 10 m/s. The velocity remains constant and then the vehicle comes to rest in 15 s. If the total distance covered is 500 m, determine from a velocity–time graph:
(a) the time travelled at constant velocity,
(b) the value of the uniform acceleration,
(c) the value of the uniform retardation,
(d) the average speed over the whole journey.

10. A vehicle starts from rest with uniform acceleration of 2 m/s² which is maintained for 40 s. The vehicle then travels at a uniform speed for 12 min, and finally slows down at a retardation of 3 m/s² and comes to rest. Determine the total distance travelled by using a velocity–time graph.

11. A train starts from a station and accelerates uniformly to a speed of 25 m/s. The distance covered during this period is 800 m. It then travels at a constant speed for the next 10 km and is brought to rest at the next station with a uniform deceleration of 0.5 m/s². Draw a velocity–time graph and from it determine:
(a) the total time of the journey,
(b) the distance between the stations,
(c) the average speed for the journey.

12. Complete the crossword puzzle of Fig. 4.8 using Chapter 4 as reference material.

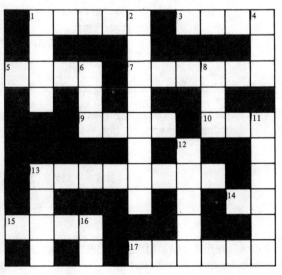

Figure 4.8

Across
1. Velocity without direction
3. SI is a system.
5. Not stationary
7. Unit of force
9. A second
10. Ne.t. ., but rearranged
13. Rate of change of displacement
14. SI in reverse
15. The space under a velocity–time diagram
17. Opposite to acceleration

Down
1. Gradient with the sixth letter omitted
2. A branch of mechanics
4. A vehicle starting from rest reaches a velocity of 40 m/s, travelling north, in 4 s. Determine the rate of acceleration assuming it to be uniform.
6. Wave motion, but rearranged
8. A body is dropped from a tower with zero initial velocity and with a final velocity of 200 m/s. Calculate the height of the tower in kilometres if the time of the fall is 2 s.
11. $ut + \frac{1}{2}at = ?$, but with the 'e' missing and in reverse
12. Opposite to finish
13. The two missing letters are the same and can be found by taking the first letter from the heading of Chapter 4.
16. Morning

4.12 Force, mass, and acceleration

Newton's second law of motion states that the rate of change of momentum of a body is proportional to the resultant force and takes place in the direction of the force:

$$\text{Force} \propto \text{rate of change of momentum}$$
$$\propto \text{mass} \times \text{rate of change of velocity}$$
$$\propto \text{mass} \times \text{acceleration}$$
$$\text{Force} = \text{constant} \times \text{mass} \times \text{acceleration}$$

Therefore

$$\text{constant} = \frac{\text{force}}{\text{mass} \times \text{acceleration}}$$

Let

Mass = 1 kilogram
Acceleration = 1 metre per second squared
Force = 1

Then the constant = 1

so force = mass × acceleration, i.e., $F = ma$

The force is measured in newtons which is that force which gives a mass of 1 kilogram an acceleration of 1 metre per second squared.

Example

1. Calculate the force that produces an accleration of 15 metres per second squared in a mass of 5 kilograms.

$m = 5$ kg
$a = 15$ m/s^2

Force = mass × acceleration
$F = ma$
$= 5 \times 15$
$= 75$ N

The force produced is 75 newtons.

2. A force of 300 newtons acts on a mass of 50 kilograms. Calculate the acceleration produced by this force.

$F = 300$ N
$m = 50$ kg

Force = mass × acceleration

Acceleration = $\dfrac{\text{force}}{\text{mass}}$

$a = \dfrac{F}{m}$

$= \dfrac{300}{50}$

$= 6$ m/s^2

The acceleration produced by a force of 300 newtons is 6 metres per second squared.

As stated in Sect. 4.6, when objects fall freely their acceleration is constant. The force exerted by the gravitational field is called its weight (not its mass) and it varies as gravity changes:

Weight = mass × acceleration due to gravity
$= mg$

3. Calculate the weight of a body having a mass of 80 kilograms given that the acceleration due to gravity is 9.81 metres per second squared.

$m = 80$ kg
$g = 9.81$ m/s^2

Weight = mass × acceleration due to gravity
$= mg$
$= 80 \times 9.81$
$= 784.8$ N

The weight of the body is 784.8 newtons

It is important to realize that mass can never change with position but weight can change with position. An example of this change was seen when humans landed on the moon, which has only one-sixth of the earth's gravity.

4. Calculate the force exerted by a container of mass 200 kilograms on the ropes of a lifting system when it is (a) raised with an acceleration of 5 metres per second squared or (b) lowered with an acceleration of 5 metres per second squared.

$m = 200$ kg
$g = 9.81$ m/s^2
$a = 5$ m/s^2

(a) Force on lifting system ropes
= force due to mass + force due to acceleration
$= ma + mg$
$= (200 \times 5) + (200 \times 9.81)$
$= 200(5 + 9.81)$
$= 200 \times 14.81$
$= 2962$ N

(b) Force exerted when container is lowered
= force due to acceleration − force due to mass
$= mg - ma$
$= (200 \times 9.81) - (200 \times 5)$
$= 200(9.81 - 5)$
$= 200 \times 4.81$
$= 962$ N

Force exerted when lifting is 2962 newtons and when dropping is 962 newtons.

4.13 Exercise

1. State the relationship between force, mass, and acceleration.
2. Explain the difference between mass and weight.
3. Calculate the force that produces an accleration of 25 m/s^2 in a mass of 12 kg.
4. A force of 500 N acts on a mass of 25 kg. Calculate the acceleration produced by this force.
5. A force of 45 N acting on a body produces an acceleration of 3 m/s^2. Determine the mass of the body.
6. A vehicle is designed to travel 3 km in 100 s. The mass of the vehicle is 2000 kg. If the vehicle starts from rest and accelerates uniformly determine: (a) the final velocity, (b) the acceleration, (c) the accelerating force.
7. Determine the force that will increase the velocity of a mass of 20 kg from 8 m/s to 28 m/s in 5 s.
8. Using the information in question 7 determine how far the mass would travel.
9. Calculate the force exerted on the floor of a lift by a man of mass 70 kg when the lift is: (a) ascending with an acceleration of 1.5 m/s^2 and (b) descending with an acceleration of 2 m/s^2.
10. Calculate the weight of a body having a mass of 40 kg if the acceleration due to gravity is 9.81 m/s^2.
11. The force causing an iron core to move into an electric solenoid is 2 N and the mass of the core is 0.3 kg. With what acceleration will it move? (CGLI)
12. A mass of 800 kg is to be uniformly accelerated at 2.5 m/s^2 against a constant resisting force of 500 N. Determine the value of the total force in newtons which must be applied. (WMAC)
13. Define acceleration.

    A load of 3000 kg is raised by a chain and is given a starting acceleration of 0.2 m/s^2. Determine the initial pull in the chain. If the acceleration is continued for 6 s, find the final velocity and the distance travelled in this time.
    (NWRAC)
14. State Newton's second law of motion.

    A body weighing 2.5 kg is moving with a velocity of 12 m/s. A uniform force acts upon it and causes its velocity to increase to 20 m/s in 4 s. Calculate: (a) the magnitude of the force, (b) the

work done by the force. (WJEC)
15. Find the force which, acting on a mass of 10 kg for 15 s, causes the mass to move through 10 m in that time.
16. A vehicle weighing 1000 kg is brought to rest in 14 m with a retardation of 2 m/s^2. Calculate the average value of the force required to stop it and the work done.

    If all the work done in stopping the vehicle is equally shared between four brakes, determine the force and torque on one of the brake drums. Each brake drum has a diameter of 0.3 m. The circumference of the wheels is 3 m and there is no slip. (YHCFE)

4.14 Wave motion

A wave, shown in Fig. 4.9, is defined as a periodic disturbance in a medium that involves the displacement of material particles. A wavelength is the distance between successive points of equal phase, i.e., the distance from crest to crest. The frequency of a wave motion is the number of cycles per second, and is measured in hertz.

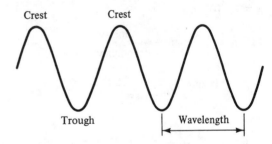

Figure 4.9

Mechanical types of waves are:
(a) waves in a liquid,
(b) sound waves in air,
(c) shock waves from earthquakes, and
(d) waves in strings or wires.
   Electromagnetic waves are:
(a) Radio, television, and microwaves,
(b) Radar waves,
(c) Infrared radiation,
(d) Ultraviolet radiation,
(e) Visible light radiation,
(f) X-radiation, and

(g) Gamma radiation.

Wavelength is equal to the velocity of the onward wave motion divided by its frequency:

$$\text{Wavelength} = \frac{\text{velocity}}{\text{frequency}}$$

$$\lambda = \frac{v}{f}$$

Examples

1. Calculate the wavelength of a wave having a velocity of 30 metres per second and a frequency of 0.3 hertz.

$v = 30$ m/s
$f = 0.3$ Hz

$$\lambda = \frac{v}{f} = \frac{30}{0.3} = 100 \text{ m}$$

The wavelength is 100 metres.

2. Calculate the frequency of a radio wave of wavelength 1500 metres and of velocity 3×10^8 metres per second.

$\lambda = 1500$ m
$v = 3 \times 10^8$ m/s

From $\quad \text{wavelength} = \dfrac{\text{velocity}}{\text{frequency}}$,

$$\text{frequency} = \frac{\text{velocity}}{\text{wavelength}}$$

so

$$f = \frac{v}{\lambda} = \frac{3 \times 10^8}{1500} = 200\,000 \text{ Hz} = 200 \text{ kHz}$$

The frequency of the radio wave is 200 kilohertz.

3. A water wave travels a distance of 0.9 metre in 3 seconds. If the wavelength is 0.05 metres determine: (a) the velocity of the wave front and (b) the wave frequency.

$t = 3$ s
$s = 0.9$ m
$\lambda = 0.05$ m

$$\text{Velocity} = \frac{\text{distance travelled}}{\text{time taken}}$$

$$v = \frac{s}{t} = \frac{0.9}{3} = 0.3 \text{ m/s}$$

$$\text{Frequency} = \frac{\text{velocity}}{\text{wavelength}}$$

$$f = \frac{v}{\lambda} = \frac{0.3}{0.05} = 6 \text{ Hz}$$

The velocity of the wave front is 0.3 metre per second with a frequency of 6 hertz.

4. An echo sounder being used at sea sends a sound pulse from the ship to the sea-bed and back in 20 milliseconds. If the velocity of sound in sea water is 1600 metres per second determine the depth of the sea below the ship.

$v = 1600$ m/s
$$t = \frac{20}{2} = 10 \text{ ms} = 0.01 \text{ s}$$

$$\text{Frequency} = \frac{1}{\text{time}} = \frac{1}{0.01} = 100 \text{ Hz}$$

$$\text{Wavelength} = \frac{\text{velocity}}{\text{frequency}}$$

$$\lambda = \frac{v}{f} = \frac{1600}{100} = 16 \text{ m}$$

The depth of sea below the ship is 16 metres.

4.15 Exercise

1. Explain what is meant by the term 'wave'.
2. Explain, using a diagram, the meaning of the terms 'wavelength' and 'frequency'.
3. Give three examples of radiated energy.
4. Calculate the wavelength of a wave having a frequency of 50 Hz and a velocity of 200 m/s.
5. Determine the frequency of a vibration of wavelength 20 m and velocity 200 m/s.
6. Calculate the velocity of a sound wave of frequency 128 Hz and wavelength 4 m.
7. Determine, from the waveform shown in Fig. 4.10, the frequency and the velocity of the wave.
8. A source of frequency 400 Hz emits waves of wavelength 0.25 m. Determine the time taken for the wave to travel 200 m.

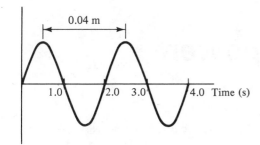

0.04 m

1.0   2.0   3.0   4.0 Time (s)

Figure 4.10

9. A wave of frequency 500 Hz travels a distance of 400 m in 5 s. Determine the number of wavelengths in the wave and the velocity of the waveform.

10. A sound wave of frequency 64 Hz travels at 165 m/s through the air. At what velocity does a sound wave of frequency 1024 Hz travel through the same air?

11. The audible range of a person is 25 Hz to 15.5 kHz. If the velocity of sound is 330 m/s, determine the longest wavelength that the person can detect.

Answers

Section 4.7
 4. 4 m/s^2
 5. 2.25 m/s^2
 6. (a) 15 s; (b) 225 m
 7. 60 m/s
 8. 313.6 m
 9. 27.78 s, 231.53 m
10. 83.3 m, 8.325 m, 852.58 s
11. 0.556 s, 1.465 m
12. (a) 40 m/s; (b) 1 m/s^2; (c) −2 m/s^2; (d) 800 m; (e) 400 m
13. (a) 437.32 m; (b) 2.775 m/s; (c) 7.247 m/s
14. (a) 960 s; (b) 48.75 km/h
15. (a) 750 m; (b) 540 s; (c) 40 km/h
16. (a) 78.48 m; (b) 39.24 m/s

17. (a) 11.47 m; (b) 1.529 s
18. 62.64 m/s
19. (a) 160.125 m; (b) 55.05 m/s

Section 4.11
 1. (a) 16 s; (b) 187.5 m; (c) 2.5 m/s
 2. (a) 45 km/h; (b) 66.67 km/h; (c) 54.29 km/h; (d) 122 km; (e) 3.2 h
 3. 6.875 m/s
 4. 2.5 m/s^2
 5. −2 m/s
 6. (a) 0.036 25 m/s^2; (b) −0.145 m/s^2
 7. 1500 m
 8. (a) 343.3 s; (b) 9.15 km; (c) 26.65 m/s
 9. (a) 25 s; (b) 0.285 7 m/s^2; (c) −0.666 6 m/s; (d) 6.66 m/s
10. 5.067 km
11. (a) 514 s; (b) 11.425 km; (c) 22.23 m/s

Section 4.13
 3. 300 N
 4. 20 m/s^2
 5. 15 kg
 6. (a) 60 m/s; (b) 0.6 m/s^2; (c) 1200 N
 7. 80 N
 8. 90 m
 9. (a) 791.7 N; (b) 581.7 N
10. 392.4 N
11. 6.66 m/s^2
12. 2500 N
13. 3003 N, 1.2 m/s, 3.6 m
14. (a) 5 N; (b) 320 N m
15. 0.888 N
16. 2000 N, 28 000 N m

Section 4.15
 4. 4 m
 5. 10 Hz
 6. 512 m/s
 7. 0.5 Hz, 0.02 m/s
 8. 2 s
 9. 2500, 80 m/s
10. 2640 m/s
11. 132 m

5 Work, energy, and power

5.1 SI units — symbols and abbreviations

Quantity	Symbol	Unit	Unit abbreviation
Acceleration due to gravity	g	metre per second squared	m/s²
Distance	d	metre	m
Energy	W	joule	J
Force	F	newton	N
Mass	m	kilogram	kg
Power	P	watt	W
Time	t	second	s
Work	W	newton metre	N m

5.2 Mechanical work done

Mechanical work is done by a force when its point of application moves in the direction of the force:

Work done = force × distance

Force (F) is measured in newtons (N), distance (d) moved in metres (m), and the work done in joules (J). A joule is the same as a newton metre.

Examples
1. Calculate the work done in moving a block 30 metres along a horizontal surface by a force of 200 newtons.

$F = 200$ N
$d = 30$ m

Work done = force × distance
= 200 × 30
= 6000 J or 6 kJ

The work done in moving the block is 6 kilojoules.

2. The work done by an electric motor is 5000 joules when a container is lifted through a vertical height of 4 metres. Determine the force required.

Work done = 5000 J
$d = 4$ m

Work done = force × distance
$W = Fd$
$\dfrac{W}{d} = F$

so $F = \dfrac{5000}{4} = 1250$ N

The force required to lift the container is 1250 newtons.

3. Calculate the work done when a mass of 6 kilograms is lifted to a height of 20 metres.

$m = 6$ kg
$d = 20$ m

Force = mass × acceleration due to gravity
= 6 × 9.81
= 58.86 N
Work done = force × distance
= 58.86 × 20
= 1177.2 J

The work done in lifting is 1177.2 joules.

4. Determine the work done by a pump in lifting 200 litres of water from the bottom of a hole 15 metres deep.

$d = 15$ m

Volume of water = 200 litres
= 200 kg (1 litre of water has a mass of 1 kilogram)
Force = mass × acceleration due to gravity
= 200 × 9.81
= 1962 N
Work done = force × distance
= 1962 × 15
= 29 430 J or 29.43 kJ

The work done by the pump is 29.43 kilojoules.

5.3 Work diagrams 📼

A work diagram, as shown in Fig. 5.1, can be obtained by plotting force against distance. The area enclosed by such a graph represents the work done. Work diagrams can take on many shapes, as shown in Fig. 5.2.

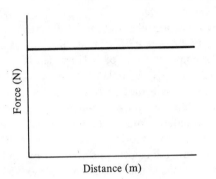

Figure 5.1

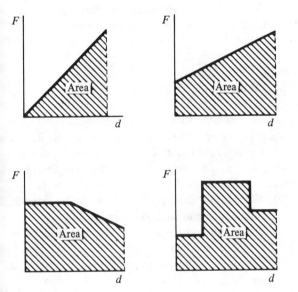

Figure 5.2

Examples

1. In a load-extension test on a spring the force was increased from 0 to 500 newtons to produce a total extension of 40 millimetres. Draw a work diagram (Fig. 5.3) and from it determine the work done in extending the spring.

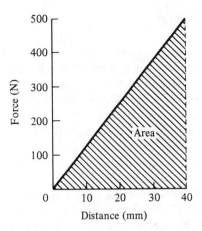

Figure 5.3

Work done = area enclosed by the graph
Area enclosed $= \frac{1}{2} \times 40 \times 500 = 10\,000$ N mm
by graph $\qquad\qquad = 10$ N m $= 10$ J

The work done in extending the spring is 10 joules.

2. A test gave the following results:

Force (N)	0	1	2	2	2	2	1.5	1	0.5	0
Distance (m)	0	2	4	6	8	10	12	14	16	18

Plot a force–distance graph (Fig. 5.4) and from it determine the work done.

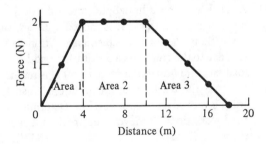

Figure 5.4

Work done = area enclosed by the graph
$\qquad\qquad$ = area 1 + area 2 + area 3
Area 1 $= \frac{1}{2} \times 4 \times 2 = 4$
Area 2 $= 6 \times 2 = 12$
Area 3 $= \frac{1}{2} \times 8 \times 2 = 8$
Work done $= 4 + 12 + 8 = 24$ N m $= 24$ J

The work done during the test is 24 joules.

5.4 Exercise

1. Define the term 'work'.
2. Calculate the work done when a block is moved with a force of 25 N for a distance of 6 m.
3. Determine the work done when a mass of 4 kg is lifted to a height of 5 m.
4. Calculate the work done when 400 litres of water are pumped from a well 30 m deep.
5. Determine what force acting through 2 m will produce 45 kJ of work.
6. Calculate the distance moved by a body when a force of 50 N produces 3000 J of work.
7. Explain what is meant by the term 'work diagram'.
8. Sketch a work diagram showing a constant force of 20 N being applied for a distance of 15 m.
9. A force increases with distance as shown in the table:

Force (N)	0	10	20	30	40	50	60	70	80	90	100
Distance (m)	0	0.2	0.4	0.6	0.8	1.0	1.5	2.0	2.5	3.0	3.5

Plot a force–distance graph and from it determine the work done.

10. A minimum force of 25 N is required in order to move a trolley along a level track. How much work is done in moving the trolley 20 m along the track?　　　　　　　　　(WJEC)
11. A truck requires a horizontal force of 100 N to move it along a track. It is moved a distance of 1 km along the track and then an additional load is added to the truck. As a result of the additional load an extra horizontal force of 50 N is required to move the truck. With the additional load the truck is moved a distance of 2 km. Determine the total work done in moving the truck and sketch the work diagram.　　　(NWRAC)
12. Define the term 'work', stating the units in which it is usually expressed. Explain how it may be represented graphically.

　　The force acting on a body varies uniformly from zero to 50 N while it moves 4 m. The force then remains constant at 50 N while the body moves a further 6 m and then decreases uniformly to zero over a final distance of 5 m. Calculate, with the aid of a suitable diagram, the total work done over the distance of 15 m.　　　(WMAC)

13. (a) The diameter of a pump piston is 15 cm and the pressure in the cylinder is 80 N/cm^2. What is the force on the piston? If the piston moves through a distance of 20 cm whilst the pressure remains constant at 80 N/cm^2, calculate the work done.
　　(b) How much work is done by pumping 5000 litres of water through a vertical distance of 30 m.　　　　　　　　　　　(WMAC)
14. How is work measured and what are the units used to measure it? The saddle of a lathe is moved by a constant force of 8 N applied to a handle which moves in a circle of diameter 180 mm. If the handle is turned 15 times, how much work is done? State the units in your answer.　　(WMAC)
15. The resultant force acting on a body in the direction of its motion increases uniformly from 10 N to 100 N over the first 20 m, and then remains constant at 100 N for the next 50 m. It then decreases uniformly to zero over the final 30 m. Draw a graph of the resultant force against distance and determine the total work done. What is the average force exerted over the whole distance?　　　　　　　　　(WMAC)

5.5 Energy

The amount of work done when an object is moved is equal to the energy expended in moving it. Energy takes many forms, and it can neither be created nor destroyed; it can only be changed from one form into another. There are five major categories of energy:
(a) Mechanical energy, which includes kinetic, potential, strain, and sound energy.
(b) Electromagnetic energy, including electrical, magnetic, and light energy.
(c) Thermodynamic energy, which is heat energy in all forms.
(d) Chemical energy, obtained by the reaction of two or more elements or compounds.
(e) Nuclear energy, which is obtained from fusion or fission processes in the nuclei of atoms.

　　Conversion of large amounts of energy takes place when electricity is being generated at a power station. The power station burns coal or oil, or uses nuclear fuel to produce heat energy. This heat energy is used to turn water into steam in a boiler. The steam then travels along pipes to a turbine. The kinetic energy of a jet of steam does work on the blades of a turbine as it strikes them. The turbine blades rotate and their rotational kinetic energy turns the rotor of an electrical generator. The windings of the generator cut a magnetic field and produce an electric current, which finds its way into factories or houses for power, heat, and light, all themselves forms of energy. There are other examples of energy conversion, e.g.:

(a) Strain energy from a wound clock spring to turn gear wheels.
(b) Potential energy from a hammer lifted to hit a nail into timber.
(c) Chemical energy converted into electrical energy in a primary or secondary cell.
(d) Electrical energy used in motors to produce mechanical energy in power tools, etc.
(e) Electromagnetic radiation energy produced by the sun in the growth of plants, producing timber or food, and, after millions of years, coal that we burn today to obtain heat energy.

5.6 Power

Power is defined as rate of transfer of energy:

$$\text{Power} = \frac{\text{energy}}{\text{time}}$$

Power (P) is measured in watts (W), time (t) in seconds (s), and the energy (W) in joules (J). Note that a joule is also the same as a watt second.

Example
1. A force of 200 newtons moves a block through a distance of 15 metres. Determine: (a) the work done and (b) the power developed if the movement takes 45 seconds.

$F = 200$ N
$d = 15$ m
$t = 45$ s

> Work done = Fd = 200 × 15 = 3000 N m
> Energy = 3000 J
> Power = $\dfrac{W}{t} = \dfrac{3000}{45}$ = 66.67 W

The work done in moving the block is 3000 joules and the power developed is 66.67 watts.

The kilowatt (kW) is used when the power is large, i.e., 1000 W = 1 kW.

5.7 Efficiency

The efficiency of any system is the ratio of work output to work input:

$$\text{Efficiency} = \frac{\text{work output}}{\text{work input}}$$

The work put into the system is always greater than the work obtained from the system, i.e., the efficiency is always less than 1. Efficiency is often quoted as a percentage:

$$\text{Efficiency} = \frac{\text{work output}}{\text{work input}} \times 100 \text{ per cent}$$

Example
1. The output of a motor is 1800 joules for an electrical input of 2500 joules. Calculate the efficiency of the system.

$$\text{Efficiency} = \frac{\text{work output}}{\text{work input}} \times 100 \text{ per cent}$$
$$= \frac{1800}{2500} \times 100 \text{ per cent} = 72 \text{ per cent}$$

The efficiency of the system is 72 per cent.

2. An electrically driven pump lifts 6000 litres of water per hour through a height of 20 metres. Calculate the input power to the motor if the overall efficiency of the pump and motor is 80 per cent.

$d = 20$ m
Volume of water = 6000 litres = 6000 kg = 60 000 N, assuming 10 N is equivalent to 1 kg.
Efficiency = 80 per cent

$$\text{Force} = 60\,000 \text{ N/h} = \frac{60\,000}{60} \text{ N/min}$$
$$= \frac{60\,000}{60 \times 60} = 16.67 \text{ N/s}$$

> Work done = force × distance
> = 16.67 × 20
> = 333.4 N m/s
> = 333.4 J/s

Because 1 joule = 1 watt second, the output power of the motor is 333.4 watts.

$$\text{Efficiency} = \frac{\text{work output}}{\text{work input}} \times 100 \text{ per cent}$$

$$80 = \frac{333.4 \times 100}{\text{work input}}$$

$$\text{Work input} = \frac{333.4 \times 100}{80}$$

$$= 416.8 \text{ W}$$

The input power to the motor is 416.8 watts.

3. An electrically operated hoist is required to raise a load of 4000 newtons through 6 metres in 2 minutes. Calculate: (a) the work done by the hoist, (b) the power developed assuming an efficiency of 100 per cent, and (c) the power developed assuming the hoist to be 60 per cent efficient.

$F = 4000 \text{ N}$
$d = 6 \text{ m}$
$t = 2 \text{ min} = 120 \text{ s}$

$$\text{Work done} = Fd = 4000 \times 6 = 24\,000 \text{ N m}$$
$$= 24\,000 \text{ J}$$

$$\text{At 100 per cent efficiency, power} = \frac{\text{energy}}{\text{time}} = \frac{24\,000}{120} = 200 \text{ W}$$

$$\text{Power input} = \text{power output} = 200 \text{ W}$$

$$\text{Efficiency} = \frac{\text{work output}}{\text{work input}} \times 100 \text{ per cent}$$

$$\text{At 60 per cent efficiency, work output} = \frac{\text{efficiency} \times \text{work input}}{100}$$

$$= \frac{60 \times 200}{100}$$

$$= 120 \text{ W}$$

The work done by the hoist is 24 000 joules, giving power developed of 200 watts at 100 per cent efficiency and 120 watts at 60 per cent efficiency.

5.8 Exercise

1. Define the term 'energy'.
2. List the five major categories of energy.
3. Give an example of a form of energy being converted into another form.
4. Define the term 'power'.
5. State two practical units of power.
6. Explain what is meant by the term 'efficiency'.
7. Determine the work done and the power developed when a force of 250 N moves a block for a distance of 2 m in a time of 50 s.
8. Calculate the power developed when a mass of 5 kg is being lifted to a height of 12 metres in 40 s.
9. Determine the power developed by a pumping system that is lifting 500 l of water from a well 16 m deep in 90 s.
10. The output of a system is 150 J for an input of 200 J. Calculate the efficiency of the system.
11. Calculate the efficiency of a machine which uses 50 J of energy and does 40 J of work.
12. The output power of an electric motor is 10 kW. Calculate the input power if the motor is 75 per cent efficient.
13. Calculate the work done by a motor in 20 min if it has an output power of 5 kW.
14. A motor is 80 per cent efficient with an output power of 12 kW. Calculate: (a) the work done by the motor in 1 hour and (b) the energy used by the motor in this time.
15. A casting weighing 500 kg is raised at a uniform speed by a crane through 12 m vertically in 15 s. At what power is the crane working? (CGLI)
16. (a) Define energy and name two different kinds of energy.
    (b) A weight of 330 kg is lifted through a height of 20 m in 6 s. Calculate: (i) the energy stored in the weight due to its having been lifted and (ii) the average power required to lift the weight. (NCFE)
17. A mass of 50 kg is raised vertically through a height of 15 m in 40 s with uniform velocity. Calculate the force required, the work done, and the power exerted. (WMAC)
18. Define work and power.
    An object is moved a distance of 8 m in 5 s along a horizontal plane by the action of a force of 10 N. Calculate the work done by the force and the power required. (NWRAC)
19. A weight of 2000 kg is to be dragged over a rough horizontal surface at 6 m/s. Find: (a) the force required and (b) the power required. (WJEC)

20. A block of stone weighing 300 kg is placed on a horizontal surface and is pulled along at a uniform speed of 8 km/h by means of a horizontal rope. Determine: (a) the force in the rope, (b) the work done in moving the block 15 m, and (c) the power expended. (WMAC)

21. A pump lifts 20 000 litres of water to a height of 250 m every hour. Calculate the power output of the pump and the work done in 16 h. (NWRAC)

22. A force of 1.5 kN acts on a plunger 175 mm in diameter. What is the average pressure on the plunger? If the plunger is used to force oil under a piston 525 mm in diameter, what would be the maximum load the piston could support? What power would be necessary to lift the load through 150 mm in 2 s? Neglect all losses. (NCFE)

23. A plunger weighing 35 kg rests at the bottom of a vertical cylinder 0.5 m in diameter. Water is pumped into the cylinder by a pump which has an average output of 750 W. Calculate: (a) the pressure necessary to raise the plunger and (b) the time required to raise the plunger through 1 m. (NCFE)

24. A train weighing 200 tonnes goes at a steady speed of 100 km/h. Determine the power which the engine must develop (1 tonne = 1000 kg). (WMAC)

25. An electric motor supplies power to a haulage gear which has to raise a total load of 10 tonnes through 3 m in 30 s. If the efficiency of the haulage system is 80 per cent, determine: (a) the power to be supplied by the motor and (b) the work lost or wasted per second when working at this efficiency. (WMAC)

26. Define the terms 'work' and 'power'.

A pump delivers 4000 litres of water through a vertical height of 110 m. What is the amount of work done? If this is accomplished in 100 s what power is developed? If the efficiency of the pump and motor is 75 per cent, what is the motor power? (EMFEC)

27. A bucket of water weighing 20 kg is pulled up a well by means of a rope 20 m long. If the rope weighs 1 kg/m and is completely wound up when the bucket reaches the surface draw a graph representing the force required to raise the bucket of water from the bottom to the top of the well.

Using the diagram, determine: (a) the work done in raising the bucket to the surface, (b) the power required if this is accomplished in 30 s, (c) the work done during the first 6 m of the rise, and (d) the work done during the last 6 m of the rise. (WMAC)

28. A load of 500 N is lifted from a shaft 200 m deep by means of a rope weighing $1\frac{1}{4}$ kg/m length. Show, by means of a graph, how the force required to raise the load varies with the distance lifted. Hence, calculate the total work done in raising the load to the surface. If the operation takes 5 min and the speed of lifting is constant, what is the average power exerted? (WMAC)

29. An electrically driven pump lifts water through a height of 40 m at the rate of 10 kN/min. If the efficiency of the pump is 65 per cent, calculate the power of the motor required to drive it.

If the motor has an efficiency of 85 per cent, what power will it take from the mains? (NCFE)

30. An electric motor is tested by means of a friction brake and it is found that when the electrical power supplied to the motor is 2 kW, the power transmitted to the brake is 1.5 kW.

Calculate: (a) the overall efficiency of the motor and (b) the heat dissipated by the brake in 1 min. (NWRAC)

31. A conveyor belt is driven by an electric motor, a force of 10 kN being required to move the loaded belt at a steady speed of 5 m/min. If the overall efficiency of the drive and the motor is 60 per cent, calculate: (a) the least input power required at the motor and (b) the cost per 7-h day if electricity costs 15 pence per unit. (NCFE)

32. A pump driven by an electric motor is required to lift 360 kN of water per hour through a height of 36 m.
    (a) Calculate the work done per minute by the pump.
    (b) If the total losses in the pump and motor are equivalent to 1.3 kW find, in kilowatts, the electrical power required to lift the water. (NCFE)

33. Complete the crossword puzzle of Fig. 5.5 using Chapter 5 as reference material.

44

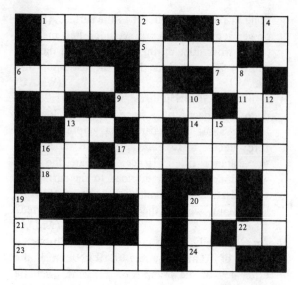

Figure 5.5

Down

1. A source of energy
2. Output/input
3. Calculate the percentage efficiency of a system if the output is 20 J and the input is 400 J.
4. All systems go
8. Abbreviation of millimetre
10. A form of energy without the 'h'
12. Nuclear energy is obtained from the fission process in the . . . . . . of atoms.
13. Calculate the force needed to move a load 10 m if the work done is 20 J.
15. Force =? × acceleration
16. A large unit of energy abbreviated
17. See Sect. 5.2, Mechanica. work .one, but with the letters reversed.
19. One watt second is equal to . . . joule.
20. The efficiency of a system can never be greater than . . .

Across

1. Work done = ? × distance
3. Calculate the work done when a load of 0.5 N is being moved 4 m.
5. The work done by an electric motor is 750 J when a container is lifted through a vertical height of 150 m. Determine the force required.
6. Energy is defined as the amount of . . . . done.
7. A unit of work
9. Power = energy/?
11. See 7 across but in reverse
13. Force is measured in new. .ns.
14. Morning
16. A large unit of power abbreviated
17. This is covered when work is being done, with the last letter removed
18. Unit of energy
20. Metre per .ec.nd — but with the letters in reverse
21. A large unit of force abbreviated and in reverse
22. A system of units
23. Can neither be created nor destroyed
24. Nucl. .r

Answers

Section 5.4

2. 150 N m
3. 196.2 N m
4. 117.7 kJ
5. 22.25 kN
6. 60 m
9. 175 J
10. 500 N m
11. 350 kN
12. 525 N m
13. (a) 14.139 kN, 2827.8 N m; (b) 1.4715 MN m
14. 67.87 N m
15. 7600 N m, 76 N

Section 5.8

7. 500 N m, 10 W
8. 14.715 W
9. 872 W
10. 75%
11. 80%

12. 13.33 kW
13. 6 MJ
14. (a) 67.87 N m; (b) 15 kWh
15. 3924 W
16. (b) (i) 64 746 J; (ii) 10 791 W
17. 490.5 N, 7357.5 N m, 183.9 W
18. 80 N m, 16 W
19. (a) 19.62 kN; (b) 117.72 kW
20. (a) 2943 N; (b) 44 145 N m; (c) 6.54 kW
21. 13.625 kW, 294.3 MN m
22. 62 355 N/m^2, 13.5 kN
    4.05 kW
23. (a) 1748 N/m^2; (b) 0.46 s
24. 54.5 MW
25. (a) 12.26 kW; (b) 73.58 kN m
26. 4316.4 × 10^3 N m, 43.164 kW, 57.552 kW
27. (a) 5886 N m; (b) 196.2 W; (c) 1354 N m;
    (d) 2178 N m
28. 345.25 kN m, 1.151 kW
29. 10.26 kW, 12.07 kW
30. (a) 75%; (b) 90 kJ
31. (a) 1.389 kW; (b) £1.46
32. 216 kN m, 4.9 kW

6   Heat energy

6.1 SI units — symbols and abbreviations

Quantity	Symbol	Unit	Unit abbreviation
Current	I	ampere	A
Electromotive force	E	volt	V
Energy, work, quantity of heat	W	joule	J
Latent heat of fusion	L	joule per kilogram	J/kg
Latent heat of vaporization	L	joule per kilogram	J/kg
Mass	m	kilogram	kg
Potential difference	V	volt	V
Power	P	watt	W
Resistance	R	ohm	Ω
Specific heat capacity	c	joule per kilogram kelvin	J/kg K
Temperature	T	kelvin	K
Time	t	second	s

6.2 Heat input

When an electric current flows through a conductor, heat is generated in it.

Examples of the heating effect of an electric current within a domestic dwelling are:

electric fire
electric iron
electric kettle
electric water heater
immersion heater
open-type radiator
tubular heater
convector heater
panel heater
electrically heated hot water radiator
under floor warming
night storage heater

The reader could probably add to this list, with a similar list being prepared for an industrial concern.

The heat produced by an electric current is proportional to:
(a) the square of the current,
(b) the resistance of the conductor,
(c) time of current flow.

$$\text{Heat energy input} = I^2 Rt$$

where I is the current in amperes
R is the resistance in ohms
t is the time in seconds

and the heat energy is in joules.

6.3 Quantity of heat output

The amount of heat required to raise the temperature of a mass of 1 kilogram of water by 1 kelvin is approximately 4200 joules, i.e., 4.2 kJ.

Heat energy output is directly proportional to the mass of the substance and the temperature change.

Therefore

Heat energy output $\propto$ mass × temperature change
Heat energy output = constant × mass × temperature change

This constant is known as the specific heat capacity (c) of the material being heated.

$$\text{Heat energy output} = mcT$$

where m is the mass of the substance in kilograms
c is the specific heat capacity in joules per kilogram kelvin
T is the temperature change in kelvin.

The specific heat capacity for water is 4200 J/kg K. Specific heat values for other materials are given in Table 6.1.

Table 6.1 Specific heat capacity (c) (J/kg K)

Substance	c	Substance	c
Air*	7.1×10^3	Iron	0.5×10^3
Ethyl alcohol	2.5×10^3	Lead	0.13×10^3
Aluminium	0.92×10^3	Mercury	0.14×10^3
Copper	0.39×10^3	Steam*	1.4×10^3
Glass	0.13×10^3	Marble	0.88×10^3
Hydrogen*	10×10^3	Oil	2.0×10^3
Ice	2.1×10^3	Wood	17×10^3

*The values quoted are for the case of constant volume.

Example

1. Determine the amount of heat required to raise the temperature of 2 kilograms of water from 17 to 100°C. The specific heat capacity of the water is 4200 joules per kilogram kelvin.

$m = 2$ kg
$T = 100 - 17 = 83\,°C = 83$ K
$c = 4200$ J/kg K

Heat required $= mcT$
$= 2 \times 4200 \times 83$
$= 697\,200$ J or 697.2 kJ

The amount of heat required is 697.2 kilojoules.

6.4 Efficiency

The efficiency of any system is the ratio of work output to work input:

$$\text{Efficiency} = \frac{\text{work output}}{\text{work input}}$$

The work put into the system is always greater than the work output, i.e., the efficiency is always less than 1. It is therefore useful to quote the efficiency as a percentage:

$$\text{Efficiency} = \frac{\text{work output}}{\text{work input}} \times 100 \text{ per cent}$$

Examples

1. Determine the efficiency of a heating system if the heat energy input is 800 kilojoules and the heat output is 600 kilojoules.

Work output = 600 kJ
Work input = 800 kJ

$$\text{Efficiency} = \frac{\text{work output}}{\text{work input}} \times 100 \text{ per cent}$$

$$= \frac{600}{800} \times 100 \text{ per cent}$$

$$= 75 \text{ per cent}$$

The efficiency of the heating system is 75 per cent.

2. Determine the efficiency of a water heater if it takes 5 minutes to boil 2 kilograms of water initially at 17°C, when the supply is 12 amperes at 240 volts.

$m = 2$ kg
$c = 4.2 \times 10^3$ J/kg K
$T = 100 - 17 = 83\,°C = 83$ K
$V = 240$ V
$I = 12$ A
$t = 5$ min $= 5 \times 60 = 300$ s

Heat energy output $= mcT$
$= 2 \times 4.2 \times 10^3 \times 83$
$= 697\,200$ J

Heat energy input $= I^2 Rt$ where $R = \dfrac{V}{I}$

$$= 12^2 \times \frac{240}{12} \times 300$$

$$= 864\,000 \text{ J}$$

$$\text{Efficiency} = \frac{\text{work output}}{\text{work input}} \times 100 \text{ per cent}$$

$$= \frac{697\,200}{864\,000} \times 100 \text{ per cent}$$

$$= 80.69 \text{ per cent}$$

The efficiency of the water heater is 80.69 per cent.

3. A water heater rated at 1 kilowatt at 240 volts contains 20 kilograms of water. Calculate the time required to raise the temperature of the water from 20 to 100°C if the efficiency of the system is 80 per cent.

$m = 20$ kg
$c = 4.2 \times 10^3$ J/kg K
$T = 100 - 20 = 80$ K
$V = 240$ V
$P = 1$ kW $= 1000$ W

From $P = VI$: $I = \dfrac{P}{V} = \dfrac{1000}{240} = 4.17$ A

Heat energy output $= mcT$

$$= 20 \times 4.2 \times 10^3 \times 80$$
$$= 6\,720\,000 \text{ J}$$

From $P = \dfrac{V^2}{R}$

$$R = \dfrac{V^2}{R} = \dfrac{240^2}{1000} = 57.6 \ \Omega$$

Heat energy input $= I^2 Rt$

$$= 4.17^2 \times 57.6 \times t$$
$$= 1001.6t$$

Efficiency $= \dfrac{\text{work output}}{\text{work input}} \times 100$ per cent

$$80 = \dfrac{6\,720\,000}{1001.6t} \times 100$$

$$t = \dfrac{6\,720\,000 \times 100}{80 \times 1001.6}$$
$$= 8387.4 \text{ s}$$
$$= 139.8 \text{ min}$$
$$= 2 \text{ h } 20 \text{ min}$$

The time taken to heat the water is 2 hours 20 minutes.

4. The temperature of 5 kilograms of water is to be raised from 15 to 59.52 °C in 30 minutes by means of an electric water heater. Determine a suitable resistance for the heater element assuming a supply voltage of 250 volts and a loss of 10 per cent of heat by radiation.

$m = 5$ kg
$c = 4.2 \times 10^3$ J/kg K
$T = 59.52 - 15 = 44.52$ K
Efficiency $= 100 - 10 = 90$ per cent
$t = 30$ min $= 30 \times 60 = 1800$ s

Heat energy output $= mcT$

$$= 5 \times 4.2 \times 10^3 \times 44.52$$
$$= 935\,000 \text{ J}$$

Heat energy input $= I^2 Rt$

$$= I^2 R \times 1800$$

Efficiency $= \dfrac{\text{work output}}{\text{work input}} \times 100$ per cent

$$90 = \dfrac{935\,000 \times 100}{I^2 R \times 1800}$$

$$I^2 R = \dfrac{935\,000 \times 100}{90 \times 1800}$$

$$I^2 R = 577.16$$

From Sect. 7.14, $P = I^2 R$

therefore $\qquad P = 577.16$ W

Also from Sect. 7.14, $P = \dfrac{V^2}{R}$

therefore $\qquad \dfrac{V^2}{R} = 577.16$

$$R = \dfrac{V^2}{577.16}$$
$$= \dfrac{240^2}{577.16}$$
$$= 99.8 \ \Omega$$

The resistance for the heater element is 99.8 ohms.

6.5 Exercise

(Assume that the specific heat capacity of water is 4200 J/kg K.)

1. Determine the efficiency of an electric kettle if it takes 4 min to boil 1.2 kg of water initially at 15 °C, when the supply is 10 A at 200 V.

   (WMAC)

2. An electric water heater of 7.2 kg capacity was tested in a workshop and the following results were obtained:

Original temperature of water	= 16 °C
Final temperature of water	= 76 °C
Voltage	= 240 V
Current	= 2.6 A
Time	= 50 min

   Calculate the efficiency of the heater.　(CGLI)

3. Make a sketch showing the working parts of a thermostat-controlled electric water heater of the free outlet type.

   A water heater of this type rated at 1000 W, 240 V contains 0.015 m³ of water. Calculate the time required to raise the temperature of the water from 20 to 85 °C if the overall efficiency is 84 per cent.　(CGLI)

4. An electric kettle takes 5 A from a 250-V supply. How long will it take to boil 1.8 kg of water from 20 to 100°C if the efficiency is 80 per cent? What is the cost of boiling the water if electrical energy costs 12 pence per kilowatt hour? (WJEC)

5. A current of 5 A passes through a coil of 20-Ω resistance for 15 min. If the heat dissipated could be entirely used in heating water, what mass of water could have its temperature raised by 50°C? (NWRAC)

6. An immersion heater has a resistance of 25 Ω and is connected to a 240-V supply. How long will it take to raise the temperature of 2.2 kg of water from 10 to 100°C if the efficiency of the process is 75 per cent? What is the cost at 15 pence per kilowatt hour? (CGLI)

7. The temperature of 4.5 kg of water is to be raised from 15 to 100°C in 20 min by means of an electric immersion heater.

    Assuming a supply voltage of 240 V and that 10 per cent of the heat produced will be lost to radiation, determine a suitable resistance for the unit. What will be the current consumption? (WMAC)

8. An electric kettle contains 1.2 kg of water, and it is required to raise the temperature of the water from 20 to 100°C in 5 min. If 80 per cent of the heat which is produced in the heating element is usefully employed in heating the water, calculate the resistance of the element, the supply being at 240 V. (NCFE)

9. How long will it take to boil 1.2 kg of water in an electric kettle if the temperature of the cold water is 20°C, the supply pressure is 200 V, and the resistance of the element 50 Ω?

    What would be the cost of boiling the water at 10 pence per kilowatt hour? Assume that 80 per cent of the electrical energy is converted into heat. (WJEC)

10. What is meant by the terms 'ohm', 'ampere', and 'volt'? State the law which connects these three together.

    The power taken by an electric kettle when used on a 240-V supply is 330 W. Determine: (a) the resistance of the heating element of the kettle, (b) the electrical energy taken by the kettle in 5 min, and (c) the quantity of water which the kettle would heat from 15°C to boiling point, in the stated time, if the whole of the electrical energy were used to heat the water. (EMFEC)

11. A heater having a resistance of 105 Ω is connected to a 210-V supply and used for 10 min to heat 1.5 kg of oil of specific heat 0.8. Assuming the efficiency of the heater to be 85 per cent, calculate the rise in temperature of the oil. (WJEC)

12. An immersion heater, having a resistance of 200 Ω, is placed in a jar containing 2 kg of water. If a current of 2 A passes through the heater for 8 min, calculate the increase in the temperature of the water, assuming an efficiency of 85 per cent. (WJEC)

13. An electric kettle takes 6 A from 250-V mains. The kettle raises 1.8 kg of water from 20°C to boiling point, 20 per cent of the energy supplied to the element being wasted in the process. Calculate the time taken for the operation. (NCFE)

14. An electric water heater has a power rating of 3 kW and its efficiency is 80 per cent. Calculate the time required to raise the temperature of 48 kg of water through 75°C. (NCFE)

15. A certain immersion heater requires 2 h to raise the temperature of 192 kg of water to boiling point when the supply voltage is 240. If the overall efficiency remains unaltered, how long will it take to bring 18 kg of water to the boil from the same initial temperature, if the supply voltage is reduced to 200? (WMAC)

16. A current of 3 A at 8 V flows for 5 min through a coil submerged in 170 g of water. If this raises the temperature of the water from 10 to 20°C, find the specific heat capacity. Assume no heat losses. (WJEC)

17. An electric heater contains 240 kg of water at 15°C and is rated at 2 kW. If the heat losses are 10 per cent of the input, find the mean temperature of the water after the heater has been switched on for 8 h. (WJEC)

18. An electric immersion heater, rated at 1 kW and connected to a 230-V supply, is placed in a tank containing 38 kg of water at a temperature of 12°C. Assuming the efficiency of the heater to be 85 per cent, calculate: (a) the time required to heat the water to a temperature of 90°C and (b) the resistance of the heater. (WJEC)

6.6 Latent heat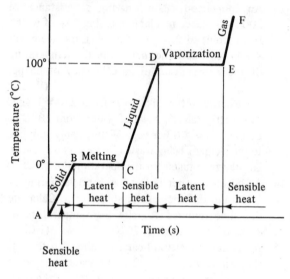

Heat which produces a change in temperature is called sensible heat. The heat absorbed or emitted during a change of state with no change in temperature is called latent heat. A typical example of this situation is when ice is changed by the addition of heat energy first into water and then into vapour. A typical temperature–time graph is shown in Fig. 6.1.

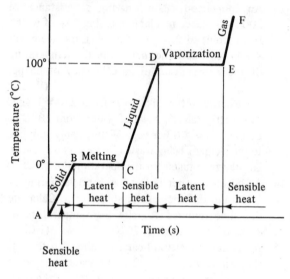

Figure 6.1

The type of heat supplied and the condition of the ice during this process is shown in Table 6.2.

Table 6.2

Point	Type of heat supplied	Temperature	Condition of ice
AB	Sensible heat	Changing from below freezing to 0 °C	Solid
BC	Latent heat	0 °C	Melting
CD	Sensible heat	Changing from 0 to 100 °C	Liquid
DE	Latent heat	100 °C	Vaporizing
EF	Sensible heat	Above 100 °C	Vapour

The heat energy absorbed or emitted during a change of state is given by the formula:

Heat energy = mass × latent heat of the material

For ice the specific latent heat of fusion is 334 kJ/kg and for water the specific latent heat of vaporization is 2260 kJ/kg. Table 6.3 gives some values of specific latent heat.

Table 6.3

Substance	Specific latent heat of fusion (kJ/kg)	Specific latent heat of vaporization (kJ/kg)
Carbon dioxide	190	367
Glycol	182	802
Mercury	11.8	286
Naphthalene	8.4	297
Oxygen	13.9	214
Aluminium	400	–
Copper	200	–
Gold	67	–
Silver	105	–
Iron	210	–

We can have a cooling curve corresponding to a heating curve, as shown in Fig. 6.2. The material under test is naphthalene. Sensible heat is given out over the range AB; latent heat is given out over the range BC as the material solidifies; finally, more sensible heat is given out over the range CD.

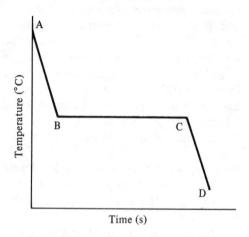

Figure 6.2

Examples
1. Calculate the amount of heat required to melt 5 kilograms of ice at its freezing point.

$m = 5$ kg
$L = 334$ kJ/kg

$$\text{Heat} = mL$$
$$= 5 \times 334$$
$$= 1670 \text{ kJ}$$

The amount of heat required to melt the ice is 1670 kilojoules.

2. How much heat energy is required to melt 10 kilograms of naphthalene at its melting point?

$m = 10$ kg
$L = 8.4$ kJ/kg

$$\text{Heat} = mL$$
$$= 10 \times 8.4$$
$$= 84 \text{ kJ}$$

The amount of heat energy required is 84 kilojoules.

3. Determine the total heat required to convert 4 kilograms of ice at $0\,^\circ$C to water at $60\,^\circ$C.

$m = 4$ kg
$T = 60 - 0 = 60$ K
Latent heat of fusion $= L = 334$ kJ/kg
Specific heat capacity of water $= c = 4.2$ kJ/kg K
Total heat required $= mL + mcT$
$$= (4 \times 334) + (4 \times 4.2 \times 60)$$
$$= 1336 + 1008$$
$$= 2344 \text{ kJ}$$

The total heat required is 2344 kilojoules.

4. Calculate the amount of heat required to convert 6 kilograms of ice at $-10\,^\circ$C to water at $65\,^\circ$C.

$m = 6$ kg
Specific heat capacity of ice $= c_1 = 2.1$ kJ/kg K
Specific heat capacity of water $= c_2 = 4.2$ kJ/kg K
Latent heat of fusion of ice $= L = 334$ kJ/kg
$T_1 = 0 - (-10) = 10$ K
$T_2 = 65 - 0 = 65$ K

Heat required $= mc_1 T_1 + mL + mc_2 T_2$
$$= (6 \times 2.1 \times 10) + (6 \times 334)$$
$$+ (6 \times 4.2 \times 65)$$
$$= 126 + 2004 + 1638$$
$$= 3768 \text{ kJ}$$

The amount of heat required is 3768 kilojoules.

6.7 Exercise

1. Define the term 'latent heat'.
2. Explain the difference between sensible heat and latent heat.

3. Explain, with the aid of a labelled sketch, the type of temperature–time graph that would be obtained when ice at below freezing point has heat applied to it until it disappears as vapour.

4. Calculate the quantities of heat required in the following cases:
   (a) to convert 10 kg of ice at $0\,^\circ$C to water at $60\,^\circ$C;
   (b) to convert 15 kg of ice at $0\,^\circ$C to steam at $100\,^\circ$C;
   (c) to convert 9 kg of ice at $-10\,^\circ$C to water at $80\,^\circ$C.

5. Determine the total heat required to convert 4 kg of ice at $-15\,^\circ$C to steam at $100\,^\circ$C.

6. Examine the graph of Fig. 6.3 showing a temperature–time graph for the heating at atmospheric pressure of a block of ice at a constant rate until boiling occurs.
   (a) How long was it after the heating started before the temperature was $50\,^\circ$C?
   (b) What is happening to the ice between points V and W?
   (c) How long after heating started did boiling begin?
   (d) What was the most rapid rate of temperature change?
   (e) How long did it take for the temperature to change from 0 to $100\,^\circ$C including latent heat?
   (f) What is happening between points Y and Z?
   (g) How long did it take for the ice, after it had reached $0\,^\circ$C, to change to water?
   (h) How long did it take for the water, after it had reached $100\,^\circ$C, to change to steam?

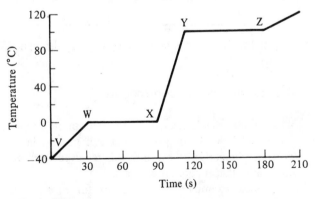

Figure 6.3

7. Explain what is meant by the statement 'the latent heat of vaporization of steam is 2260 kJ/kg'.

8. Explain what is meant by the statement 'the latent heat of fusion of ice is 334 kJ/kg'.

9. Examine the diagram drawn in Fig. 6.4, which represents a temperature–time graph for the heating of a block of ice initially at a temperature of −15 °C.

Redraw the following table and complete it with a √ to indicate which parts of the graph are showing sensible heat and which latent heat.

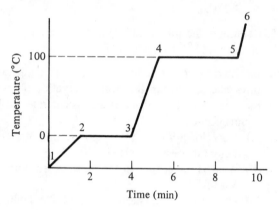

Figure 6.4

Graph	Sensible heat	Latent heat
1–2		
2–3		
3–4		
4–5		
5–6		

List the three states that the ice is going through.

6.8 Expansion and contraction

When a material is heated in any one of its three states, solid, liquid or gas, it increases in size, i.e., expands. Similarly, if heat energy is removed from a material so that it cools, it contracts.

Practical examples of allowances for expansion and contraction are:

(a) The gaps in concrete road sections to allow for seasonal changes in temperature.

(b) Lap joints in railway lines to compensate for temperature change.

(c) Overhead electricity supply cables are designed so that they sag in summer and tighten in winter and this does not put excessive stress on the fixing points.

(d) Steel bridges are placed on rollers to allow for expansion and contraction.

(e) Hot water systems in industry and domestic dwellings which need to take into account expansion when the pipes are hot and contraction when the weather is freezing.

(f) Bi-metallic strips, which use differential expansion to close and open thermostat switches.

(g) Thermometers use the expansion of liquid to indicate temperature.

(h) Internal combustion engines use the expansion of heated gases to move a piston, which in turn rotates the driving shaft and moves the vehicle.

(i) Sheet metal fabrications joined together by hot rivets which contract and tighten on cooling.

The reader should add examples from home, industry, and commerce to this list.

6.9 Exercise

1. State why lengths of domestic hot water pipes often have a loop in them.

2. Explain why, after an increase in temperature, a railway line does not buckle.

3. Consider two strips of metal fixed together which are heated at a constant rate. State what will happen to both metals.

4. When hot water is poured into a glass it may crack. Explain why this is so.

5. What happens to the volume of a metal block if it is heated?

6. After a discussion with your class teacher make a list of the useful applications of heat causing expansion of materials.

7. Complete the crossword puzzle of Fig. 6.5 using Chapter 6 as reference material.

Figure 6.5

Across

1. The formula for heat energy output
4. One of the states of a material
5. Measured in amperes
8. The second and fourth letters of resistance
9. The value for water is 4.2 kJ/kg K, but only the first word.
12. When a body is contracting is it losing or gaining heat?
13. The second and fourth letters of energy
15. One form of energy
17. The specific heat capacity of this substance is 2 kJ/kg K.
18. The fourth and sixth letter of kilogram
19. Overhead electricity supply cables are designed so that they . . . in summer and tighten in winter
21. When ice is heated it me. .s.
22. The specific latent heat of fusion is 67 kJ/kg.
24. Is there a temperature change when latent heat is being used?
25. This four-letter word, in reverse, carries a substance of latent heat of vaporization of 2260 kJ/kg.

Down

1. Measured in kilograms
2. The heat absorbed or emitted during a change of state with no change in temperature is called the latent heat of . . . . . .

3. Calculate the amount of heat (MJ) required to melt 3 kg of ice at its freezing point. The latent heat of fusion of ice is 334 kJ/kg.
6. Lap joints in these compensate for temperature change
7. Measured in seconds
10. Rate of doing work
11. Naphthalene is reaching this condition in Sec. 6.5.
14. Gaps in concrete . . . . sections allow for seasonal changes in temperature
15. It gets this when the temperature rises.
16. Determine the amount of heat (MJ) required to raise the temperature of 8 kg of water from 40 to 100 °C. The specific heat capacity of water is 4.2 kJ/kg K. Hint: use the nearest whole number.
20. This is needed in many constructions to allow for expansion.
22. Kil. .ram with the missing letters in reverse

Answers

Section 6.5

1. 89.25%
2. 96.90%
3. 81.25 min
4. 10.08 min, 2.52p
5. 2.143 kg
6. 8.02 min, 4.62p
7. 38.72 Ω, 6.2 A
8. 34.29 Ω
9. 10.5 min, 1.4p
10. (a) 174.6 Ω; (b) 0.027 5 kW h; (c) 0.277 3 kg
11. 29.75 K
12. 38.86 K
13. 8.4 min
14. 105 min
15. 13.5 min
16. 4.235 kJ/kg K
17. 66.43 °C
18. (a) 244 min 6 s; (b) 52.9 Ω

Section 6.7

4. (a) 5860 kJ; (b) 45 210 kJ; (c) 6408 kJ
5. 12 308 kJ
6. (a) 102 s; (c) 112 s; (e) 82 s; (g) 60 s; (h) 68 s

7 Principles of electricity

7.1 SI units — symbols and abbreviations

Quantity	Symbol	Unit	Unit abbreviation
Area	a	square metre	m^2
Energy, work, quantity of heat	W	joule	J
Electromotive force	E	volt	V
Force	F	newton	N
Length	l	metre	m
Magnetic flux density	B	tesla	T
Potential difference	V	volt	V
Power	P	watt	W
Resistance	R	ohm	Ω
Resistivity	ρ	ohm metre	Ωm
Time	t	second	s
Quantity of electricity, electric charge	Q	coulomb	C

When making circuit diagrams in electrical engineering it is necessary to use symbols to denote the various components. We use the internationally agreed British Standard graphical symbols, which have the advantage that anyone examining a diagram can recognize the symbols used, thus making it unnecessary to refer to a new list of symbols on each occasion.

A selection of British Standard graphical symbols is shown in Fig. 7.2. A complete list of graphical symbols for electrical and electronic diagrams can be found in British Standard 3939.

7.2 British Standard graphical symbols

A circuit diagram is a diagram which shows by means of symbols the components and their interconnections concerned in the operation of a circuit. The aim should be to show the operation of the circuit as clearly as possible; circuit diagrams do not necessarily show the best physical layout of the components and their connections. A simple series circuit is shown in Fig. 7.1.

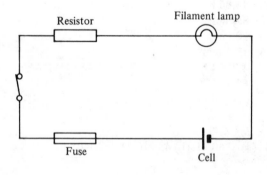

Resistor Filament lamp

Fuse Cell

Figure 7.1

7.3 Electric current

An electric current (I) measured in amperes (A) is the result of the movement of electrons through a material in one direction. The negatively charged electron is so small that it takes many millions of electrons to make up one coulomb (C) of electric charge. The relationship between charge (Q), current (I), and time (t) is:

$$Q = It$$

Examples
1. Calculate the quantity of electrical charge when a steady current of 5 amperes flows into a material for 20 seconds.

$I = 5$ A
$t = 20$ s

$$Q = It$$
$$= 5 \times 20$$
$$= 100 \text{ C}$$

The quantity of electrical charge is 100 coulombs.

Description	Symbol	Description	Symbol
Primary or secondary cell		Resistor with moving contact	
Battery of primary or secondary cells: alternative symbol		Heater	
Battery with tappings		Signal lamp: general symbol	
Filament lamp		Winding with core	
Discharge lamp: general symbol		Transformer	
Cold cathode discharge lamp, e.g., neon lamp		Generator	G
Hot cathode tubular fluorescent lamp		pnp transistor	
Earth		Ammeter	A
Electric bell: general symbol		Voltmeter	V
Electric buzzer		Wattmeter	W
Siren		Ohmmeter	Ω
Horn		Oscilloscope	osc
Fuse		Galvanometer	
Capacitor: general symbol		Clock	
Polarized capacitor: general symbol		Alternating current or voltage	
Polarized electrolytic capacitor		Time switch	
Winding: general symbol, i.e., inductor, coil, choke coil, or inductive reactor		Switch: general symbol (normally open)	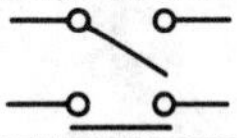
Fixed resistor: general symbol		Switch: general symbol (normally closed)	
		pn junction diode	

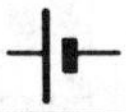

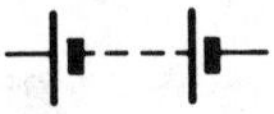

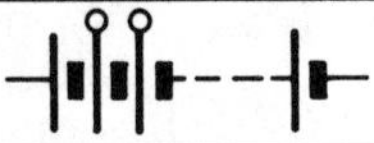

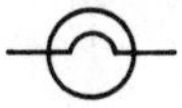

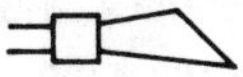

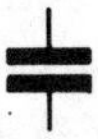

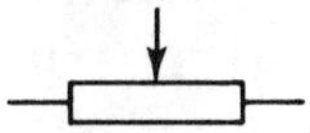

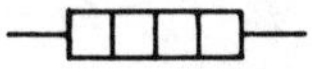

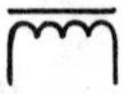

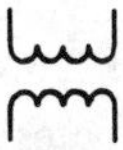

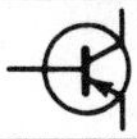

Figure 7.2

2. Determine the electric current flowing when a charge of 20 000 coulombs is supplied in 2 hours.

$Q = 20\,000$ C
$t = 2\,h = 2 \times 60 \times 60 = 7200$ s

$$I = \frac{Q}{t}$$

$$= \frac{20\,000}{7200}$$

$$= 2.78 \text{ A}$$

The current flowing is 2.78 amperes.

3. Calculate the time for the flow of a current of 20 milliamperes to result in a charge of 4 coulombs.

$I = 20$ mA $= 20 \times 10^{-3}$ A
$Q = 4$ C

$$t = \frac{Q}{I}$$

$$= \frac{4}{20 \times 10^{-3}}$$

$$= \frac{4 \times 10^3}{20}$$

$$= \frac{4000}{20}$$

$$= 200 \text{ s}$$

The time needed is 200 seconds.

7.4 Exercise

1. The sketch in Fig. 7.3 shows an outline circuit diagram. Redraw the circuit and label the component parts as shown by the arrows.   (NCFE)

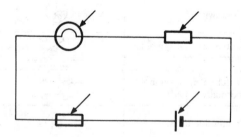

Figure 7.3

2. Complete the circuit diagram of Fig. 7.4 so that the three resistors are connected in series and the total current flow can be measured by an ammeter and the potential difference across the cell can be measured by a voltmeter.   (NCFE)

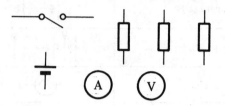

Figure 7.4

3. Complete the series circuit diagram of Fig. 7.5 so that the potential difference across the lamp can be measured.   (NCFE)

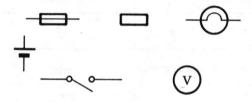

Figure 7.5

4. Draw a circuit diagram showing two bells connected in parallel controlled by a single bell push. Include a fuse and one cell in the circuit. (NCFE)
5. Sketch a circuit diagram showing a lamp controlled by two single-pole two-way switches. (NCFE)
6. A circuit consists of four lamps, two controlled by one switch and two by another. Draw a circuit diagram using British Standard symbols for this circuit. A fuse, neutral link, and an earth terminal should be included.   (NCFE)
7. A circuit consists of two resistors connected in parallel. Sketch a diagram of the circuit to include a cell, a fuse, and a single-pole switch. Show on the diagram a voltmeter to measure the cell terminal voltage and an ammeter to measure the current flowing through one of the resistors.   (YHCFE)
8. Draw a labelled circuit diagram using British Standard graphical symbols showing how a relay may be used in a bell circuit when the bell is a long distance from the bell push. Describe what happens when the bell push is pressed.   (WJEC)

9. Draw a well-labelled circuit diagram using British Standard graphical symbols showing a cell, a single-pole switch, a fuse, and three resistors in series. Show on the diagram a voltmeter measuring the cell terminal voltage. (WJEC)

10. Draw a well-labelled circuit diagram, using British Standard graphical symbols, showing three bells connected in parallel controlled by a single bell push. Include a fuse and one cell. (WJEC)

11. Draw a circuit diagram showing a cell, a fuse, a bell push, and a bell connected in series. Include in the circuit an ammeter to measure total current flow and a voltmeter to measure the potential difference of the cell. (NCFE)

12. Calculate the quantity of electrical charge when a steady current of 3 A flows for 25 s.

13. Determine the charge when a current of 10 A flows for 20 min.

14. Find the electrical charge when a current of 1.5 A flows for 2 h.

15. Calculate the time in minutes for a flow of 15 A which results in a charge of 5400 C.

16. Determine the current when a charge of 3500 C accumulates in 35 s.

17. Determine the charge resulting from a current of 450 mA for 2.5 min.

18. Find the time needed for a current of 25 μA to result in a charge of 3 C.

19. A current of 5 A is passed through two copper plates immersed in a solution of copper for 1 h. Determine the resulting charge.

20. Determine the current required to deposit silver on a cathode in a solution of silver nitrate if the operation takes 2 h and uses a charge of 5500 C.

21. A gold-plating bath operates with a steady current of 20 A. Determine the time taken to plate bars with a charge of 1200 C.

22. An electric charge of 40 C flows past a point in an electric circuit in 6 min. Calculate: (a) the amount of current flowing and (b) the charge that results in a time of 30 s if the current remains constant.

7.5 Electromotive force

For electric current to flow in a circuit, two conditions are necessary: a continuous circuit and a force to move the electrons. A device such as a simple cell provides the force to move the electrons round the circuit. The maximum force available is given a special name: electromotive force (abbreviation e.m.f.) (E), measured in volts (V).

7.6 Resistance and Ohm's law 📼

Loads such as lamps, water heaters, etc., when placed in an electrical circuit, oppose the flow of electrons. This opposition is called resistance (R) and is measured in ohms (Ω). Resistance is equal to the voltage at the terminals of a resistor divided by the current flowing through it:

$$\text{Resistance} = \frac{\text{voltage}}{\text{current}} \quad \text{or} \quad R = \frac{V}{I}$$

The voltage is given the name 'potential difference'. It is measured in terms of the work done in transferring a charge from one point to another.

Ohm's law states that the potential difference across the terminals of a pure resistor is directly proportional to the current flowing through the resistor.

That is,

$$\text{potential difference } (V) \propto \text{current } (I)$$
$$V = IR$$

Examples
1. Calculate the resistance of a coil with a potential difference across it of 12 volts and a current flow of 2 amperes.

$V = 12 \text{ V}$
$I = 2 \text{ A}$

$$R = \frac{V}{I}$$

$$= \frac{12}{2}$$

$$= 6 \, \Omega$$

The coil resistance is 6 ohms.

2. A potential difference of 240 volts is applied across the terminals of a 30-ohm resistor. Determine the current flowing through the resistor.

$V = 240$ V
$R = 30\ \Omega$

$$I = \frac{V}{R}$$

$$= \frac{240}{30}$$

$$= 8\ \text{A}$$

The current flowing through the resistor is 8 amperes.

3. Calculate the potential difference across a lamp if its resistance is 50 ohms and the current flowing through it is 2 amperes.

$R = 50\ \Omega$
$I = 2$ A

$$V = IR$$
$$= 2 \times 50$$
$$= 100\ \text{V}$$

The potential difference across the lamp is 100 volts.

7.7 Linear and non-linear components

A graph of the relationship between potential difference (V) and current (I) for a single linear resistor may be obtained by investigation using the circuit in Fig. 7.6.

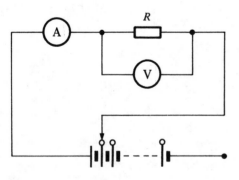

Figure 7.6

It is important to note that the ammeter is always connected in series with the component and that the voltmeter is connected across the component. The potential difference across the resistor is varied by using a d.c. variable supply. A typical set of results are shown in Table 7.1.

Table 7.1

Potential difference, volts	0	2	4	6	8	10	12
Current, amperes	0	0.1	0.2	0.3	0.4	0.5	0.6

The graph of potential difference (V) versus current (I) is shown in Fig. 7.7.

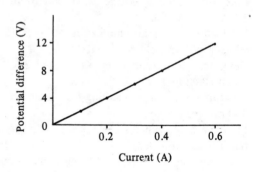

Figure 7.7

A graph of the relationship between potential difference (V) and current (I) for a non-linear component, such as a lamp, may be obtained by investigation using the circuit as in Fig. 7.6 except that the lamp replaces the resistor. A typical set of results are shown in Table 7.2.

Table 7.2

Potential difference (V)	0	2	4	6	8	10	12
Current (A)	0	0.02	0.04	0.11	0.22	0.38	0.60

The graph of potential difference versus current is shown in Fig. 7.8.

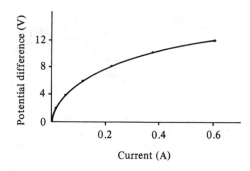

Figure 7.8

7.8 Exercise

1. An electric heating element has a resistance of 40 Ω and is to operate on a 240-V direct current supply. Calculate the current taken by the heater.
2. A cable of resistance 0.04 Ω carries a current of 50 A. Determine the potential difference across the ends of the cable.
3. A lamp is rated at 12 V 3.5 A. What is its resistance?
4. What will be the current flow when a 24-Ω resistor is connected across a 2-V supply?
5. A solenoid has a resistance of 400 Ω. Calculate the current through the solenoid when it is connected across a 120-V supply.
6. A 12-V battery is connected across a 3.5-Ω resistor. Calculate the current flowing.
7. A lamp is connected to a 240-V supply. The current taken when it is first switched on is 2 A, and when the filament becomes hot is 1.5 A. Determine the resistance of the lamp initially and when it is hot.
8. The current through the field windings of a motor is 1.8 A when the resistance is 100 Ω. After 5 min the resistance rises to 120 Ω. If the potential difference remains constant determine the new value of current flow.
9. A contactor coil of resistance 200 Ω has a current flowing through it of 0.5 A. If the supply voltage remains constant determine the current flow when the coil resistance is: (a) 210 Ω, (b) 220 Ω, (c) 230 Ω, (d) 240 Ω, and (e) 250 Ω.

10. The current flowing through a resistor is 5 A when the potential difference across it is 60 V. Determine: (a) the potential difference when the current is 7 A and (b) the current when the potential difference is 35 V.
11. A length of two-core cable has a resistance of 0.4 Ω for each conductor. What will be the voltage drop when the cable carries a current of 25 A?   (NWRAC)
12. A circuit has a resistance of 20 Ω. Calculate: (a) the current flowing when a potential difference of 260 V is applied to the circuit; (b) the current which would flow if the applied potential difference were reduced to 200 V. What added resistance is required to reduce the current to 5 A when 260 V are applied?   (WMAC)
13. If a voltmeter has a resistance of 25 kΩ, calculate the current absorbed when it is connected across a 415-V supply.
14. A test on a resistor gave the following results:

Potential difference (V)	0	25	50	75	100	125	150	175
Current (A)	0	1	2	3	4	5	6	7

Plot the graph showing the relationship between the potential difference and the current.

Is the resistor used in the test linear or non-linear? Give a reason for your answer.

15. The following readings of potential difference and current relate to an electric heater element:

Potential difference (V)	0	5	10	15	20	25	30	35
Current (A)	0	1.5	3.0	4.5	6.0	7.5	9.0	10.5

Plot a graph and determine from it:
(a) the resistance of the electric heater element,
(b) the current when the potential difference is 17 V, and
(c) the potential difference when the current is 9.5 A.

16. A test on a lamp gave the following results:

Potential difference (V)	0	3	6	9	12	15	18
Current (A)	0	0.1	0.4	1.5	3.3	5.6	8.0

Plot a graph and from it deduce whether the resistance of the lamp is linear or non-linear. Give a reason for your choice.

17. A test on a linear and a non-linear resistor gave the following readings:

Potential difference (V)	0	1	2	3	4	5	6
(Linear resistance) Current (mA)	0	4.0	8.0	12.0	16.0	20.0	24.0
(Non-linear resistance) Current (mA)	0	1.0	2.0	12.5	20.5	35.5	52.0

Plot graphs of current to a common base of potential difference. Comment on the shapes of the graphs obtained.

For each value of potential difference calculate the resistance of the linear and non-linear resistor and then plot graphs of resistance to a common base of potential difference. Comment on the shapes of the graphs obtained.

18. The following table shows the current and voltage readings obtained in an experiment to find the value of an unknown constant resistance:

Volts	2.2	5	7	9.4	11
Amperes	1	2	3	4	4.5

Draw a circuit diagram to show the apparatus that would be used for this experiment.

Plot the results on graph paper, and from the graph find the value of the resistance.

Find how much power this resistor will dissipate when connected to a battery of voltage 4 V.
(EMFEC)

7.9 Resistors connected in series

In a series circuit the resistors are connected one after the other so that the same current must flow through each resistor. Figure 7.9 shows two resistors connected in series; these can be replaced by a single equivalent resistance.

From the circuit diagram:

$E = V_1 + V_2$
$IR = IR_1 + IR_2$
$IR = I(R_1 + R_2)$
$R = R_1 + R_2$

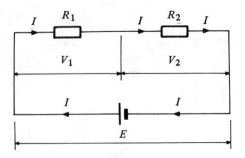

becomes

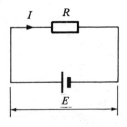

Figure 7.9

The equivalent resistance (R) of resistors connected in series is given by $R = R_1 + R_2 + \ldots + R_n$.

Examples

1. Determine the equivalent resistance of a circuit made up of three resistors of value 10, 20 and 30 Ω respectively connected in series.

$R_1 = 10\ \Omega$
$R_2 = 20\ \Omega$
$R_3 = 30\ \Omega$

$$R = R_1 + R_2 + R_3$$
$$= 10 + 20 + 30$$
$$= 60\ \Omega$$

The total resistance of the circuit is 60 ohms.

2. Two resistors of 4 and 6 Ω are connected in series across a 2-V supply. Calculate:
   (a) the total circuit resistance,
   (b) the circuit current,
   (c) the potential difference across each resistor.
   Draw a circuit diagram (Fig. 7.10).

$R_1 = 4\ \Omega$
$R_2 = 6\ \Omega$
$E = 2\ V$

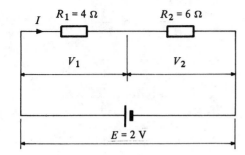

Figure 7.10

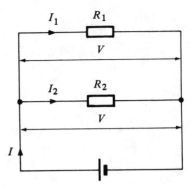

Figure 7.11

(a) $R = R_1 + R_2$
        $= 4 + 6$
        $= 10\ \Omega$

(b) $I = \dfrac{E}{R}$

        $= \dfrac{2}{10}$

        $= 0.2\ \text{A}$

(c) $V_1 = IR_1$
        $= 0.2 \times 4$
        $= 0.8\ \text{V}$
        $V_2 = IR_2$
        $= 0.2 \times 6$
        $= 1.2\ \text{V}$

Check: $E = V_1 + V_2$
        $2 = 0.8 + 1.2$
        $2 = 2$

The total circuit resistance is 10 ohms with a circuit current of 0.2 ampere. The potential difference across R_1 is 0.8 volt and across R_2 is 1.2 volts.

7.10 Resistors connected in parallel 📼

When resistors are connected in parallel the same potential difference is across each resistor, as shown in Fig. 7.11. The current flowing through each branch resistor is determined by the branch resistance and the potential difference across that branch. The total circuit current is the sum of the individual branch currents.

Any group of resistors connected in parallel can be replaced by a single equivalent resistor R. From the circuit diagram:

$$I = I_1 + I_2$$

With a single equivalent resistor:

$$I = \dfrac{V}{R}$$

and $I_1 = \dfrac{V}{R_1}$ and $I_2 = \dfrac{V}{R_2}$

Then from $I = I_1 + I_2$:

$$\dfrac{V}{R} = \dfrac{V}{R_1} + \dfrac{V}{R_2}$$

$$\dfrac{V}{R} = V\left(\dfrac{1}{R_1} + \dfrac{1}{R_2}\right)$$

$$\dfrac{1}{R} = \dfrac{1}{R_1} + \dfrac{1}{R_2}$$

The reciprocal of the equivalent resistance (R) of resistors connected in parallel is

$$\dfrac{1}{R} = \dfrac{1}{R_1} + \dfrac{1}{R_2} + \ldots + \dfrac{1}{R_n}.$$

Examples
1. Calculate the total resistance of two resistors of value 2 and 4 ohms connected in parallel.

   $R_1 = 2\ \Omega$
   $R_2 = 4\ \Omega$

62

$$\frac{1}{R} = \frac{1}{R_1} + \frac{1}{R_2}$$

$$= \frac{1}{2} + \frac{1}{4}$$

$$= \frac{4 + 2}{8}$$

$$\frac{1}{R} = \frac{6}{8}$$

Therefore $\quad R = \frac{8}{6}$

$$= 1.33\ \Omega$$

The total circuit resistance is 1.33 ohms.

2. Three resistors of value 4, 8, and 24 ohms are connected in parallel across a 24-volt d.c. supply. Calculate:
(a) the total circuit resistance,
(b) the current through each resistor,
(c) the total circuit current.
Draw a circuit diagram.

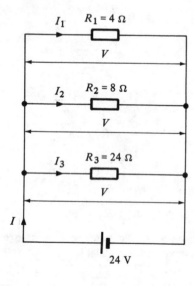

Figure 7.12

$R_1 = 4\ \Omega$
$R_2 = 8\ \Omega$
$R_3 = 24\ \Omega$
$V = 24\ V$

(a)
$$\frac{1}{R} = \frac{1}{R_1} + \frac{1}{R_2} + \frac{1}{R_3}$$

$$= \frac{1}{4} + \frac{1}{8} + \frac{1}{24}$$

$$= \frac{6 + 3 + 1}{24}$$

$$\frac{1}{R} = \frac{10}{24}$$

Therefore $\quad R = \frac{24}{10}$

$$= 2.4\ \Omega$$

(b)
$$I_1 = \frac{V}{R_1}$$

$$= \frac{24}{4}$$

$$= 6\ A$$

$$I_2 = \frac{V}{R_2}$$

$$= \frac{24}{8}$$

$$= 3\ A$$

$$I_3 = \frac{V}{R_3}$$

$$= \frac{24}{24}$$

$$= 1\ A$$

Check: $\quad I = I_1 + I_2 + I_3$
$$10 = 6 + 3 + 1$$
$$10 = 10$$

(c)
$$I = \frac{V}{R}$$

$$= \frac{24}{2.4}$$

$$= 10\ A$$

The total circuit resistance is 2.4 ohms with a total current of 10 amperes. The current flowing through the resistors is 6, 3, and 1 amperes respectively.

7.11 Exercise

1. Determine the total resistance of a circuit made up of two resistors of value 2.5 and 7.5 Ω connected in series.
2. Two resistors connected in series give a total resistance of 456 Ω. If one resistor is of value 245 Ω determine the value of the other.
3. Determine the total resistance of a circuit made up of each of the following combinations:
   (a) 72, 50, and 81 Ω,
   (b) 2.75, 6.57, 4.25, and 7.89 Ω,
   (c) 50 kΩ, 900 Ω, and 750 Ω,
   (d) 0.5 MΩ, 2.6 MΩ, and 45 kΩ.
4. A motor winding connected to a 240-V supply takes a current of 5 A. Determine the value of a resistor to be placed in series with the motor winding to reduce the current to 2 A.
5. Two resistors of value 4 and 8 Ω are connected in series across a 12-V supply. Calculate:

   (a) the total circuit resistance,
   (b) the total current flow,
   (c) the potential difference across each resistor,
   (d) the power absorbed by each resistor,
   (e) the energy used when current flows for 10 min.
6. Four resistors are connected in series with a total current flow of 5 mA. The potential differences across the resistors are 30, 40, 50, and 120 V. Calculate:
   (a) the total potential difference,
   (b) the value of each resistor in ohms and kilohms.
   (c) the total circuit resistance,
   (d) the power consumed by each resistor.

7. A circuit consists of three resistors of 12, 18, and 20 Ω connected in series. The combined circuit is connected across a supply of 100 V. Calculate: (a) the potential difference across each resistor and (b) the current taken from the supply. (NWRAC)
8. Two resistances of 4 and 16 Ω are connected in series across a 40-V supply. Calculate the current flow in the circuit and the voltage drop across the 16-Ω resistance. (EMFEC)
9. Four resistors of 10, 20, 22, and 28 Ω are all connected in series with a battery. A voltmeter is connected across the 22-Ω resistor and reads 11 V. Calculate:
   (a) the terminal voltage of the battery,
   (b) the voltage across each resistor,
   (c) the open-circuit voltage of the battery if it has an internal resistance of 2 Ω.   (CGLI)
10. Three resistors of 2, 6, and x ohms are connected in series across a 128-V supply. The voltage drop across the 2-Ω resistor is 16 V. Find:
    (a) the current flowing,
    (b) the voltage drop across the x-ohm resistor,
    (c) the ohmic value of resistor x.   (NWRAC)
11. Three resistors of value 1.47, 3.71, and 4.82 Ω are connected in series across a battery of e.m.f. 5 V. Draw a circuit diagram and calculate: (a) the total current flowing, (b) the potential difference across each resistor.   (NWRAC)
12. Calculate the equivalent resistance of the following resistors connected in parallel:
    (a) 10 and 20 Ω,
    (b) 5, 10, and 15 Ω,
    (c) 12, 16, and 24 Ω,
    (d) 40, 40, 40, and 40 Ω.
13. Two resistors of value 8 and 12 Ω are connected in parallel to a supply voltage of 24 V. Calculate:
    (a) total circuit resistance,
    (b) the current flowing through each resistor,
    (c) the total power dissipated.
14. Two resistors of value 2 and 3 Ω are connected in parallel. Calculate the value of a third resistor connected in parallel to give a total equivalent resistance of 1 Ω.
15. Four identical resistors are connected in parallel; the total resistance is 5 Ω. If the applied voltage is 120 V determine:
    (a) the total current,
    (b) the value of a single resistor,
    (c) the current flowing through each resistor,
    (d) the energy consumed by the circuit when current flows for 10 min.
16. State Ohm's law.
    A resistance of 100 Ω and a resistance of 40 Ω are connected in parallel across a direct current supply of 24 V. Sketch the circuit and find the current in each resistor. What is the total power consumed in watts?   (EMFEC)
17. Coils of resistance 22 and 66 Ω may be connected to a 220-V supply in series or in parallel.

64

Calculate:
(a) the current flowing through each coil for both types of connection,
(b) the power dissipated in watts in the greater resistance in the case of the series connection. (NWRAC)

18. Three resistors of 6, 8, and 12 Ω are connected in parallel and thence to a source of supply. If a current of 10 A flows through the circuit, calculate the current flowing through each resistor. (WMAC)

19. Three coils of resistance 8, 12, and 24 Ω respectively are joined in (a) series and (b) parallel. What is their joint resistance for each grouping? What current would flow in each case if the group were connected to a 44-V supply? (NWRAC)

20. A circuit of 5-Ω resistance comprises a 7-Ω coil in parallel with another coil. Calculate the resistance of the other coil.

    If a total current of 3 A passes through the circuit, calculate the current in, and the power absorbed by, each coil. (NWRAC)

21. Two coils, of resistance 4 and 6 Ω respectively, are connected in parallel. Calculate the resistance of a third coil to be placed in parallel with them so that 5000 W may be dissipated in the circuit when it is connected to a 100-V supply. (WJEC)

22. State Ohm's law.

    Two resistors each of 40 Ω are supplied from a fixed 240-V supply. Determine the total current taken from the supply and the potential difference across each of the two resistors when they are connected (a) in series and (b) in parallel. (NWRAC)

23. Two resistors of 4 and 8 Ω are connected in parallel across a 12-V supply. Calculate: (a) the combined resistance, (b) the current flowing in each resistance, (c) the power consumed by the circuit. (NWRAC)

24. Two resistors, A of value 15 Ω and B of unknown value, are connected in parallel to a 120-V d.c. supply. If the total current flowing is found to be 20 A, determine: (a) the value of resistor B and (b) the current in each resistor. (WMAC)

7.12 Resistance and materials 📟

The resistance of a conductor depends upon four factors:
(a) the length of the conductor,
(b) the cross-sectional area of the conductor,
(c) the type of material in use,
(d) the temperature of the material.

(a) A graph of the relationship between resistance (R) and length (l) of a material is shown in Fig. 7.13.

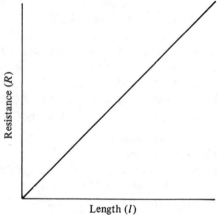

Figure 7.13

(b) A graph of the relationship between resistance (R) and cross-sectional area (a) of a material is shown in Fig. 7.14.

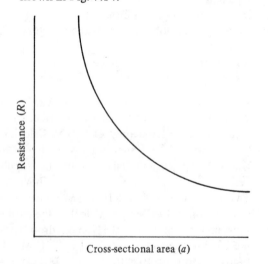

Figure 7.14

(c) From the graphs in Figs 7.13 and 7.14:

$$\text{Resistance} \propto \frac{\text{length}}{\text{cross-sectional area}}$$

$$R = \text{constant} \times \frac{l}{a}$$

This constant factor depends upon the type of material in use and is called resistivity; the symbol is ρ (rho). The resistivity of a material is defined as the resistance at unit length and unit cross-sectional area. Then

$$R = \frac{\rho l}{a}$$

It is important that when resistance is being calculated that all units must be compatible. For example, the length in metres means that the cross-sectional area must be in square metres. For the resistance in ohms the resistivity must then be in ohm metres.

(d) The resistance of a material changes with a change in temperature. For an increase in temperature:
  (i) the resistance of pure metals, e.g., silver, copper, aluminium, and iron, increases,
  (ii) the resistance of insulators, e.g., PVC, rubber, asbestos, glass, and paper will be relatively unaffected,
  (iii) the resistance of electrolytes, e.g., acids, alkalis, and salts, and of carbon, silicon, and germanium will decrease.
A few metal alloys, such as constanton and eureka, have a resistance which alters very little with temperature. Graphs of resistance to a base of temperature for conductors, insulators, and semiconductors are shown in Fig. 7.15.

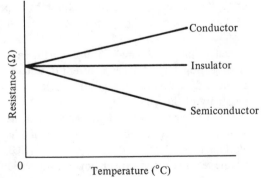

Conductor

Insulator

Semiconductor

Resistance (Ω)

0   Temperature (°C)

Figure 7.15

Examples
1. Calculate the resistance of 4 metres of wire having a cross-sectional area of 2.5 square millimetres if the resistivity of the material is 1 microhm metre.

$l = 4$ m
$a = 2.5$ mm^2 = 2.5×10^{-6} m^2
$\rho = 1\ \mu\Omega$ m = $1 \times 10^{-6}\ \Omega$ m

$$R = \frac{\rho l}{a}$$

$$= \frac{1 \times 10^{-6} \times 4}{2.5 \times 10^{-6}}$$

$$= \frac{4}{2.5}$$

$$= 1.6\ \Omega$$

The resistance of the wire is 1.6 ohms.

2. A coil is wound with 2000 turns of wire, the mean length of each turn being 100 millimetres. Calculate the cross-sectional area of the wire so that the coil carries a current of 5 amperes from a 100 volt d.c. supply. The resistivity of the material is 0.02 microhm metre.

$I = 5$ A
$V = 100$ V
$l = 2000 \times 100$ mm = $2000 \times 100 \times 10^{-3}$ m
$\rho = 0.02 \times 10^{-6}\ \Omega$ m

$$R = \frac{V}{I} = \frac{100}{5} = 20\ \Omega$$

From

$$R = \frac{\rho l}{a},$$

$$a = \frac{\rho l}{R}$$

$$= \frac{0.02 \times 10^{-6} \times 2000 \times 100 \times 10^{-3}}{20}$$

$$= 0.02 \times 100 \times 100 \times 10^{-9}$$

$$= 0.000\ 000\ 2\ \text{m}^2$$

$$= 0.000\ 000\ 2 \times 10^6\ \text{mm}^2$$

$$= 0.2\ \text{mm}^2$$

The cross-sectional area of the wire is 0.2 square millimetres.

3. Calculate the length of a wire, 1.5 millimetres in diameter, which has a resistance of 30 ohms. The resistivity of the wire material is 0.017 microhm metre.

$d = 1.5$ mm

$R = 30\ \Omega$

$\rho = 0.017\ \mu\Omega$ m $= 0.017 \times 10^3\ \mu\Omega$ mm

$\quad = 0.017 \times 10^3 \times 10^{-6}\ \Omega$ mm

$$a = \frac{\pi d^2}{4} = \frac{3.142 \times 1.5 \times 1.5}{4} = 1.767\ \text{mm}^2$$

From

$$R = \frac{\rho l}{a},\quad l = \frac{aR}{\rho}$$

$$= \frac{1.767 \times 30}{0.017 \times 10^3 \times 10^{-6}}$$

$$= \frac{3118 \times 10^6}{10^3}$$

$$= 3\,118\,000\ \text{mm}$$

$$= 3118\ \text{m}$$

The length of the wire is 3118 metres.

7.13 Exercise

1. State the relationship between the resistance of a conductor and its length, cross-sectional area, and resistivity.

2. State the general relationship between the resistance of a material and changes in temperature.

3. Draw a graph of temperature against resistance for (a) a conductor, (b) an insulator, and (c) a semiconducting material.

4. Calculate the resistance of 20 m of wire, 4 mm² in cross-sectional area, if the resistivity of the wire material is 0.023 $\mu\Omega$ m.

5. A coil is wound with 300 m of copper wire. Calculate the cross-sectional area of the wire if the resistance is 25 Ω. Resistivity of copper is 0.02 $\mu\Omega$ m.

6. Determine the resistance of 25 m of wire, 1 mm in diameter, if the material resistivity is 17.5 $\mu\Omega$ mm.

7. (a) Calculate the resistance of relay coil that takes 6 A from a 36-V d.c. supply.
   (b) Calculate the length of the relay coil given

that the cross-sectional area of the coil wire is 0.2 mm² and the material resistivity is $1.72 \times 10^{-8}\ \Omega$ m.

8. Calculate the resistivity of 200 m of aluminium wire of resistance 12 Ω and 0.5 mm² in cross-sectional area.

9. (a) Calculate the quantity of electricity delivered by a wire carrying a current of 10 A for 5 min. If the potential difference between its ends is 60 V, calculate the energy converted and the cost of the energy at 4p/kW h.
   (b) What is the resistivity of the material of this wire if it is 100 m long and 0.5 mm in radius? (EMFEC)

10. (a) Give the relationship between the resistance of a conductor and the various factors which affect this value of resistance.
    (b) Calculate the length of a nickel-chrome wire, 0.381 mm in diameter, which would be required for the element of a 1 kW 250 V heater. Take the resistivity of nickel-chrome as 1016 $\mu\Omega$ mm. (WJEC)

11. (a) State how the resistance of electrical conductors of the same material varies: (i) with length, (ii) with cross-sectional area.
    (b) What length of manganin wire, having a uniform cross-sectional area of 2.5 mm², will be required to provide a resistance of 2.5 Ω?
    The resistivity of manganin may be taken as 45 microhm millimetre units. (WMAC)

12. A relay coil of 200 turns is wound using wire of diameter 1 mm. If the mean length per turn is 45 mm find the resistance of the coil ($\rho = 18\ \mu\Omega$ mm).
    What will be the effect on the coil resistance of (a) increasing the number of turns by 5 per cent and (b) increasing the diameter of the wire? (EMFEC)

13. A coil of insulated wire 155 m in length and of cross-section 1 mm² takes a current of 5 A when connected to a d.c. supply of 60 V. Calculate the resistivity of the wire.
    If the above wire were of copper, what changes would you expect to observe at the end of a long working period? (CGLI)

14. Define resistivity and explain how the dimensions of a conductor affect its resistance.

A length of wire 110 m long and 1.2 mm in diameter is wound on a bobbin to form a resistor. If the wire has a resistivity of 17 $\mu\Omega$ mm, determine the value of its resistance. (NWRAC)

15. Define resistivity.

Calculate the resistance of a 100 m length of single-core copper cable whose conductor has a cross-sectional area of 1.2 mm^2, if the resistivity of copper is 17 $\mu\Omega$ mm. If the cable carries a current of 0.5 A, what is the volt drop in it per 100-m length? (WJEC)

16. Calculate the resistance of a 40-m length of copper cable, 2 mm in diameter, if the resistivity of copper is 17 $\mu\Omega$ mm. If this cable carries 5 A when fully loaded, what voltage drop occurs between the two ends? (NWRAC)

17. (a) Discuss, qualitatively, the mechanism of electrical conduction in metals. Explain the concept of resistance.

(b) Define resistivity.

(c) A wire of diameter 0.5 mm has a resistance of 2 Ω. It is drawn out to twice its original length while retaining its original volume. Calculate the new resistance of the wire. (NWRAC)

18. Define the term resistivity. In a test on a 10 cm strip of copper, the resistance was found to be 171 $\mu\Omega$. The average cross-sectional area was 9.92 mm^2. Calculate the resistivity. (NCFE)

19. Calculate the cross-sectional area of a copper conductor 500 m long such that it may carry 400 A with a volts drop of 10 V.

Determine also the power loss in the cable and the heat generated in one minute. (Resistivity of copper = 0.67 $\mu\Omega$ mm.) (WJEC)

7.14 Electrical power

Mechanical work is done by a force when its point of application moves in the direction of the force for a given time:

$$\text{Work done} = \text{force} \times \text{distance moved}$$

Electrical energy is defined as the amount of work done. In an electrical circuit, when an electrical charge is set in motion by an electromotive force the charge receives energy. The charge does work in moving along a conductor:

$$\text{Electrical energy} = E \times Q$$

From Sec. 7.3, $Q = It$. Therefore:

$$\text{Electrical energy} = E \times It$$
$$W = EIt \quad \text{or} \quad W = VIt$$

Power is defined as the rate of consuming or producing energy:

$$\text{Power} = \frac{\text{energy used}}{\text{time}}$$

$$P = \frac{W}{t}$$

Therefore
$$P = \frac{VIt}{t}$$
$$= VI$$

Power is measured in watts (W), kilowatts (kW), or megawatts (MW).

From Ohm's law, $V = IR$, so substitute IR into $P = VI$:

$$P = IRI$$
$$= I^2R$$

Likewise from Ohm's law:

$$I = \frac{V}{R}$$

so substitute $\frac{V}{R}$ into $P = VI$:

$$P = \frac{VV}{R}$$
$$= \frac{V^2}{R}$$

Therefore $P = VI$ or $P = I^2R$ or $P = \dfrac{V^2}{R}$.

Examples

1. Calculate the power input to a motor taking 8 amperes from a 250-volt d.c. supply.

$I = 8$ A
$V = 250$ V

$$P = VI$$
$$= 250 \times 8$$
$$= 2000 \text{ W}$$
$$= 2 \text{ kW}$$

The power input to the motor is 2 kilowatts.

2. A cable carrying a current of 20 amperes has a total resistance of 1.5 ohms. Determine the power absorbed by the cable.

$I = 20$ A
$R = 1.5$ Ω

$$P = I^2 R$$
$$= 20 \times 20 \times 1.5$$
$$= 600 \text{ W}$$

The power absorbed by the cable is 600 watts.

3. Determine the power absorbed by a 20-ohm resistor connected across a 2-volt d.c. supply.
$R = 20$ Ω
$V = 2$ V

$$P = \frac{V^2}{R}$$
$$= \frac{2 \times 2}{20}$$
$$= \frac{4}{20}$$
$$= 0.2 \text{ W}$$
$$= 200 \text{ mW}$$

The power absorbed by the resistor is 200 milliwatts.

4. Calculate the current flowing through a 4-ohm resistor which dissipates 100 watts.

$R = 4$ Ω
$P = 100$ W

From $P = I^2 R$, $I^2 = \dfrac{P}{R}$, and $I = \sqrt{\dfrac{P}{R}}$:

$$I = \sqrt{\frac{100}{4}}$$
$$= \sqrt{25}$$
$$= 5 \text{ A}$$

The current flowing is 5 amperes.

7.15 Fuse protection of plug tops

A fuse is a device for opening a circuit by means of a fuse element designed to melt when an excessive current flows. The fuse normally consists of a fuse-base and a fuse-link. The fuse-link may take the form of a cartridge or a carrier supporting a fuse-element.

In a 13-ampere plug top a cartridge fuse is used. From the power rating of an appliance the maximum current consumed can be calculated using the formula:

$$\text{Current} = \frac{\text{power}}{\text{potential difference}} \quad \text{or} \quad I = \frac{P}{V}$$

Fuses are available in 3 ampere and 13 ampere ratings.

Examples
1. Calculate the most suitable fuse size for a portable drill rated at 400 watts used on a 240-volt supply.

$P = 400$ W
$V = 240$ V

$$I = \frac{P}{V}$$
$$= \frac{400}{240}$$
$$= 1.67 \text{ A}$$

A suitable fuse would be one rated at 3 amperes.

2. A kettle is rated at 3 kilowatts on a 240-volt supply. Determine the required fuse size.

$P = 3$ kW $= 3000$ W
$V = 240$ V

$$I = \frac{P}{V}$$
$$= \frac{3000}{240}$$
$$= 12.5 \text{ A}$$

The plug top would be fitted with a 13-ampere fuse.

7.16 Exercise

1. An electric iron element carries a current of 2.5 A when connected across a 240-V supply. Calculate the power used.

2. Calculate the current taken from a 2-kW heater being used on a 250-V supply.
3. Calculate the potential difference across a resistor carrying a current of 27 A and consuming 8 kW.
4. Calculate the power absorbed by a heater of resistance 10 Ω when a current of 5 A is flowing.
5. Calculate the current flowing through a 500-Ω resistor rated at 8 kW.
6. A current of 1.6 A is flowing through a resistor. Determine the value of the resistor when the power absorbed is 60 W.
7. A coil has a resistance of 700 Ω. Calculate the power absorbed by this coil from a 24-V direct current supply.
8. Calculate the resistance of a 48-W 12-V lamp.
9. Calculate the potential difference across a 65-Ω resistor rated at 20 W.
10. Complete the table. All of the appliances are connected to a 240-V supply.

Appliance	Power rating	Current (A)
Fire	2 kW	
Iron	200 W	
Resistor	5 W	
Toaster	550 W	
Coffee percolator	250 W	
Immersion heater	3 kW	
Kettle	2.5 kW	
Lamp	100 W	
Radiator	6 kW	
Storage heater	8 kW	

11. Determine the most suitable fuse for a hand lamp rated at 150 W at 240 V.
12. A 2-kW fire is for use on a 250-V supply. Determine the correct fuse for use in the fire.
13. Can a 3-A fuse be used in a hand electric drill rated at 500 W and used on a 200-V supply? Give a reason for your answer.
14. Complete the table by calculating the current flowing through each appliance and stating the most appropriate fuse for the plug top.

Appliance	Power rating	Supply	Current	Suitable fuse
Fire	3 kW	250 V		
Television	525 W	240 V		
Lamp	150 W	110 V		
Kettle	2.5 kW	240 V		
Heater	2 kW	250 V		
Drill	350 W	110 V		
Hair dryer	100 W	240 V		
Coffee percolator	440 W	225 V		
Food mixer	250 W	230 V		
Hotplate	1 kW	250 V		

7.17 Permanent magnets

The magnetic field for a permanent magnet, i.e., a magnet which requires no electric current to maintain its field, is shown in Fig. 7.16.

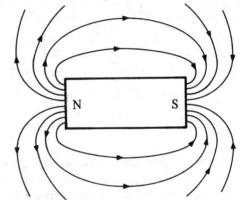

Figure 7.16

A more intense magnetic field is shown in Fig. 7.17.

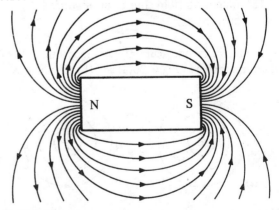

Figure 7.17

The magnetic field produced by two bar magnets with unlike poles adjacent is shown in Fig. 7.18.

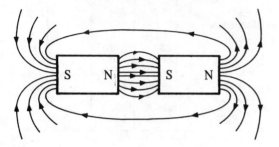

Figure 7.18

The magnetic field produced by two bar magnets with like poles adjacent is shown in Fig. 7.19.

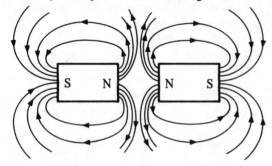

Figure 7.19

When freely suspended, a magnet orientates its axis north to south; if it is dipped into iron filings, the filings will cling to the poles; like poles repel and unlike poles attract one another.

7.18 Magnetic field due to an electric current

A conductor carrying current has a magnetic field of the form shown in Fig. 7.20(a) and (b). The magnetic field is circular; the direction of the field depends on the direction of the current.

The right-hand rule identifies the direction of the lines of magnetic flux. The conductor is gripped in the right hand with the thumb pointing in the direction of current flow. The fingers then indicate the direction of the lines of magnetic flux around the conductor. The shape of the field produced by a single-turn coil is shown in Fig. 7.21.

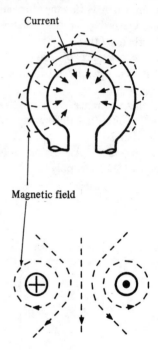

Figure 7.21

The conventional representation of an electric current flowing out of the page is a dot and into the page a cross. Two conductors carrying current will repel one another. The magnetic field produced round a solenoid is shown in Fig. 7.22.

7.19 Force acting on a conductor carrying current

The force (F) on the conductor is directly proportional to the current (I) and the length (l) of the conductor in the magnetic field:

$$F \propto l\,I$$
$$F = \text{constant} \times l\,I$$

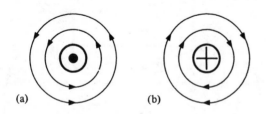

(a)   (b)

Figure 7.20

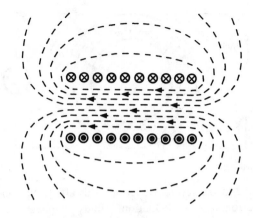

Figure 7.22

The constant factor is the magnetic flux density (*B*) of the uniform magnetic field. Therefore:

$$F = B l I$$

7.20 Moving-coil meter

The moving-coil meter depends upon the interaction of two magnetic fields, one from a permanent magnet and the other from a coil carrying current. The interaction of the two magnetic fields is shown in Fig. 7.23.

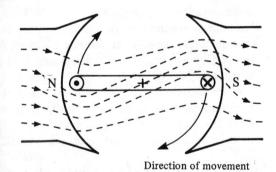

Direction of movement

Figure 7.23

The current flowing through the coil sets up a magnetic field which strengthens the existing magnetic field on the lower left-hand side and weakens it on the upper left-hand side. On the right-hand side the upper field is strengthened and the lower field is weakened. If the coil is pivoted at its centre it will tend to turn. A pointer is attached to the pivot; a

graduated scale is added and a control spring controls the rotation. Thus the distance through which the pointer moves is a measure of the current flowing through the coil. Figure 7.24 shows the coil, pointer, scale, etc.

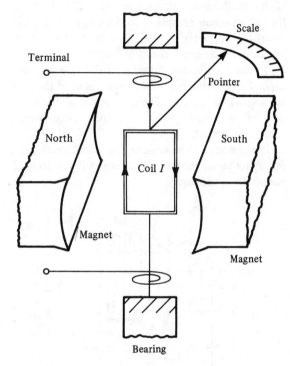

Figure 7.24

7.21 Electromagnetic induction

It was discovered by Michael Faraday that whenever there is relative movement between a conductor and a magnetic field an e.m.f. is induced in the conductor.

This effect can be demonstrated (see Fig. 7.25) by

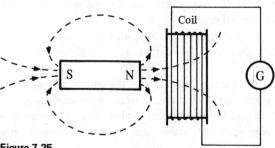

Figure 7.25

connecting a coil to a galvanometer, which is a sensitive current-detecting device, and moving a permanent magnet up to the coil. The coil cuts the magnetic field and this induces an e.m.f. in it, indicated by movement of the pointer of the galvanometer. Immediately the magnet ceases to move, the pointer of the galvanometer returns to its original zero position. When the magnet is moved away from the coil the galvanometer pointer moves in the reverse direction. This indicates that the direction of the induced e.m.f. depends upon the direction of movement of the magnet relative to the coil. The same effect is observed if the coil is moved towards and then away from a stationary magnet.

The magnet can be replaced by a coil connnected through a switch to a cell as shown in Fig. 7.26 without affecting the result.

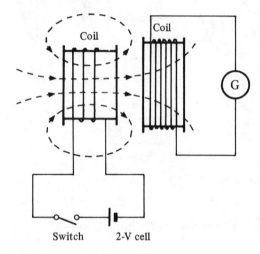

Figure 7.26

When the switch is closed, the galvanometer pointer moves. At the instant the switch is opened the pointer moves in the reverse direction. Thus the coil has the same effect on the galvanometer as the permanent magnet.

To increase the intensity of the magnetic field an iron core can be inserted in the coil as shown in Fig. 7.27.

When the switch is closed, the current in coil 1 sets up a magnetic field, which becomes linked with coil 2. This flux sets up an e.m.f. which deflects the galvanometer pointer. When the switch is opened, the magnetic field disappears and an e.m.f. is induced in

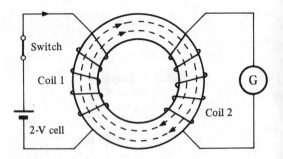

Figure 7.27

coil 2 in the reverse direction. This effect, known as electromagnetic induction, finds application in transformers.

7.22 Exercise

1. Describe, with the aid of a sketch, the type of magnetic field produced by a permanent magnet.
2. Draw a sketch to show the lines of force when two similar magnets are placed: (a) with like poles near to one another and (b) with unlike poles placed near to one another.
3. Draw diagrams showing the magnetic field in the vicinity of: (a) a single conductor and (b) a solenoid. Show in each diagram the direction of the magnetic field and current. Indicate the correct polarity of the solenoid.   (WMAC)
4. Write down an expression for the force acting on a conductor of length 1 m carrying a current I amperes, lying in and at right angles to a magnetic field of flux density B tesla.   (EMFEC)
5. A current-carrying conductor is placed at right angles to a magnetic field. Show the direction in which the force exerted on the conductor acts for a given direction of the field and current.   (WJEC)
6. State Faraday's law of electromagnetic induction.
    A straight conductor moves through a magnetic field at right angles to the field. Show by means of a diagram the direction of the induced e.m.f. relative to the field and the motion of the conductor.   (NWRAC)
7. Describe, with the aid of a sketch, the construction and action of a moving-coil instrument.
8. Complete the crossword puzzle of Fig. 7.28 using Chapter 7 as reference material.

Figure 7.28

9. Complete the crossword puzzle of Fig. 7.29 using Chapter 7 as reference material.

Figure 7.29

Across
 1. Rate of doing work
 5. Amount of work done
 7. A type of electric shock
 9. A lot of electrical installation work takes place here.
 10. Nearly a small unit of current
 13. Unit of resistance
 14. Ohm's . . .
 16. Source of electromotive force
 19. Resistors are often connected in this manner.

Down
 1. A type of voltage
 2. Unit of power
 3. Opposition to electron flow
 4. Resistance = resistivity × ?/area
 6. Opposite to stop
 8. A measuring device, printed in reverse
 11. Opposite of a high voltage
 12. Part of a magnet
 15. Morning
 17. Temp. .ature
 18. Part of a lamp

Across
 2. This component resists electron flow.
 6. Part of a coil, i.e., forget the last letter
 7. The second and sixth letter in current but in reverse
 8. $\dfrac{1}{R} = \dfrac{1}{R_1} + \dfrac{1}{R_2}$
 11. Not more than one
 13. Morning
 14. A system of units but in reverse
 15. Abbreviation for potential difference
 17. *VIt*
 19. There is little change in the resistance of this material with a change in temperature. Remove the first two letters to complete the clue.
 22. Power does this.

Down
 1. A voltmeter is always connected in this manner.
 3. This type of formula is in use: $R = R_1 + R_2$.

4. Calculate the power (kW) input to a motor taking 4 A from a 250-V d.c. supply.
5. Something to do with the right hand and Sec. 7.18.
9. A resistor is often called this.
10. Calculate the quantity of charge when a steady current of 50 mA flows into a material for 20 s.
12. A circuit must be this before it can work.
16. The formula for power gives the first two letters and a formula from Ohm's law for current gives the last two letters.
18. The third letter, seventh letter, and the last letter from constanton
20. A type of current
21. Current supplied from a battery with the letters reversed

Answers

Section 7.4
12. 75 C
13. 12 000 C
14. 10 800 C
15. 6 min
16. 100 A
17. 67.5 C
18. 0.12 µs
19. 0.77 A
21. 1 min
22. (a) 0.11 A;
    (b) 3.33 C

Section 7.8
1. 6 A
2. 2 V
3. 3.43 Ω
4. 0.083 A
5. 0.3 A
6. 0.34 A
7. 120 Ω,
   160 Ω
8. 1.5 A
9. (a) 0.48 A;
   (b) 0.46 A;
   (c) 0.44 A;

(d) 0.42 A;
(e) 0.40 A
10. (a) 84 V;
    (b) 2.92 A
11. 20 V
12. (a) 13 A;
    (b) 10 A, 32 Ω
13. 16.6 mA
14. Linear
15. (a) 3.33 Ω;
    (b) 5.1 A;
    (c) 31.67 V
16. Non-linear
18. 2.4 Ω, 6.66 W

Section 7.11
1. 10 Ω
2. 211 Ω
3. (a) 203 Ω;
   (b) 21.46 Ω;
   (c) 51.65 kΩ;
   (d) 3.145 MΩ
4. 72 Ω
5. (a) 12 Ω;
   (b) 1 A;
   (c) 4 V, 8 V;
   (d) 4 W, 8 W;
   (e) 7.2 kJ
6. (a) 240 V;
   (b) 6 kΩ, 8 kΩ, 10 kΩ, 24 kΩ;
   (c) 48 kΩ;
   (d) 150 mW, 200 mW, 250 mW, 600 mW
7. (a) 24 V, 36 V, 40 V;
   (b) 2 A
8. 2 A, 32 V
9. (a) 40 V;
   (b) 5 V, 10 V, 11 V, 14 V;
   (c) 41 V
10. (a) 8 A;
    (b) 64 V;
    (c) 8 Ω
11. (a) 0.5 A;
    (b) 0.753 V, 1.855 V, 2.41 V
12. (a) 6.67 Ω;
    (b) 2.73 Ω;
    (c) 5.33 Ω;
    (d) 10 Ω

13. (a) 4.8 Ω;
  (b) 3 A, 2 A;
  (c) 120 W
14. 6 Ω
15. (a) 24 A;
  (b) 20 Ω;
  (c) 6 A;
  (d) 1.728 MJ
16. 0.24 A, 0.6 A, 20.16 W
17. (a) Series 2.5 A, Parallel 10 A, 3.33 A;
  (b) 412.5 W
18. 4.44 A, 3.33 A, 2.22 A
19. 44 Ω, 4 Ω, 1 A, 11 A
20. 17.5 Ω, 2.14 A, 0.86 A, 32.2 W, 12.9 W
21. 12 Ω
22. 3 A, 120 V, 120 V, 12 A, 240 V
23. (a) 2.67 Ω;
  (b) 3 A, 1.5 A;
  (c) 54 W
24. (a) 10 Ω,
  (b) 8 A, 12 A

Section 7.13
4. 0.115 Ω
5. 0.2 mm^2
6. 0.56 Ω
7. (a) 6 Ω;
  (b) 69.77 m
8. 3 μΩ mm
9. (a) 3000 C, 0.05 kW h, 0.2 p;
  (b) 0.047 μΩ mm
10. (b) 7.02 m
11. (b) 139 m
12. 0.21 Ω

13. 77.4 μΩ mm
14. 1.65 Ω
15. 1.42 Ω, 0.355 V
16. 0.22 Ω, 5.5 V
17. (c) 8 Ω
18. 16.96 μΩ mm
19. 13.4 mm^2, 4 kW, 240 kJ

Section 7.16
1. 600 W
2. 8 A
3. 296.3 V
4. 250 W
5. 4 A
6. 23.44 Ω
7. 0.82 W
8. 3 Ω
9. 36.1 V
10. 8.33 A, 0.83 A, 0.021 A, 2.29 A, 1.042 A, 12.5 A, 10.42 A, 0.42 A, 25 A, 33.33 A
11. 3 A
12. 13 A
13. Yes, because the current flow is 2.5 A.

14.	12 A	13 A
	2.12 A	3 A
	1.36 A	3 A
	10.42 A	13 A
	8 A	13 A
	3.18 A	13 A
	0.42 A	3 A
	1.96 A	3 A
	1.09 A	3 A
	4 A	13 A

8 Properties of light rays

8.1 SI units – symbols and abbreviations

Quantity	Symbol	Unit	Unit abbreviation
Incidence, angle of	i	degree	°
Refraction, angle of	r	degree	°
Refractive index	μ	no unit	

The unit degree is outside the SI system but is nevertheless recognized for use with the International System.

8.2 Nature of light

Electromagnetic radiation within a band of wavelengths between approximately 3.8×10^{-7} metres and 7.6×10^{-7} metres (380 to 760 nanometres) is visible as light, the type of light depending on the wavelength. The direction in which the light energy is propagated can be represented in any diagram by a straight line, and this line is known as a ray. Further details of the spectrum of electromagnetic radiation are shown in Table 8.1.

8.3 Laws of reflection

When light energy travelling in one medium strikes the surface of another, some of the energy is reflected. If the surface of the second medium is plane (i.e., truly flat), the reflected light obeys two laws, as shown in Fig. 8.1.

The two laws of reflection are:

1. The angle of incidence (i) is equal to the angle of reflection (r).
2. The incident ray, normal, and reflected ray lie in the same plane.

Note that the angles of incidence and reflection are measured from the normal and not the surface.

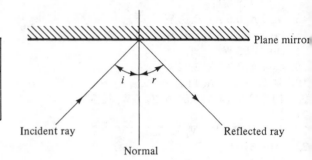

Figure 8.1

8.4 Image formation in a plane mirror

Any image produced by an optical system can be described by using a selection of the following features:

(a) the position of the image in relation to the position of the object,
(b) the real or virtual image,
(c) the upright or inverted image,
(d) the size of the image compared to the size of the object.

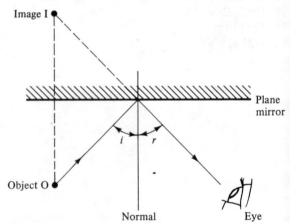

Figure 8.2

The image produced in a plane mirror can be seen in Fig. 8.2. The features of the image are:

Table 8.1 Spectrum of electromagnetic radiation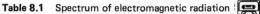

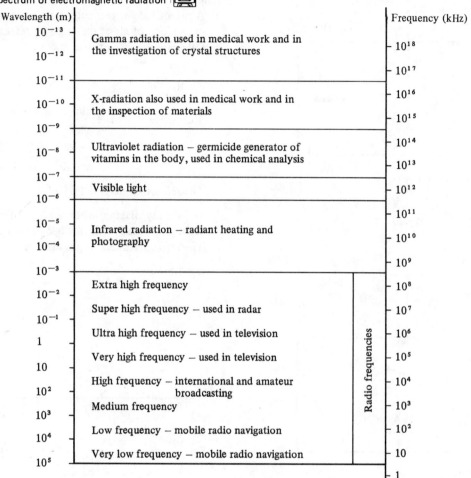

Wavelength (m)		Frequency (kHz)
10^{-13}	Gamma radiation used in medical work and in the investigation of crystal structures	10^{18}
10^{-12}		
10^{-11}		10^{17}
10^{-10}	X-radiation also used in medical work and in the inspection of materials	10^{16}
10^{-9}		10^{15}
10^{-8}	Ultraviolet radiation – germicide generator of vitamins in the body, used in chemical analysis	10^{14}
10^{-7}		10^{13}
10^{-6}	Visible light	10^{12}
10^{-5}		10^{11}
10^{-4}	Infrared radiation – radiant heating and photography	10^{10}
10^{-3}		10^{9}
10^{-2}	Extra high frequency	10^{8}
10^{-1}	Super high frequency – used in radar	10^{7}
1	Ultra high frequency – used in television	10^{6}
10	Very high frequency – used in television	10^{5}
10^{2}	High frequency – international and amateur broadcasting	10^{4}
10^{3}	Medium frequency	10^{3}
10^{4}	Low frequency – mobile radio navigation	10^{2}
10^{5}	Very low frequency – mobile radio navigation	10
		1

(the block from Extra high frequency to Very low frequency is labelled "Radio frequencies")

(a) The image is as far behind the mirror as the object is in front.

(b) The image is virtual because it could not be produced on a screen placed at I.

(c) The image is upright but reversed longitudinally.

(d) The image is the same size as the object.

8.5 Refraction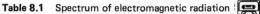

The refraction of light is the change of direction that a ray undergoes when it leaves one transparent medium and enters another. Examples of ray paths are shown in Fig. 8.3(a) and (b).

The two laws of refraction are:

1. The incident ray, normal, and refracted ray all lie in the same plane.

2. The ratio of the sine of the angle of incidence to the sine of the angle of refraction is a constant for any two media. This constant is called the refractive index and is referred to as Snell's law, i.e.:

$$\text{Refractive index } \mu = \frac{\sin i}{\sin r}$$

where i = angle of incidence and r = angle of refraction.

One aspect of refraction is that it tends to make submerged objects seem to be nearer to the surface than they really are. This effect is shown in Fig. 8.4.

78

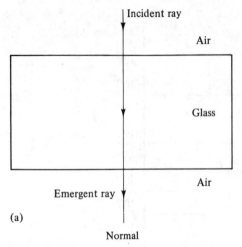

(a)

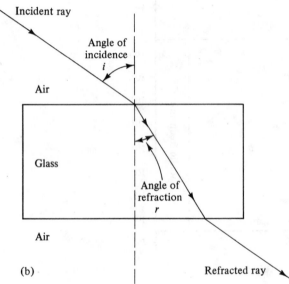

(b)

Figure 8.3

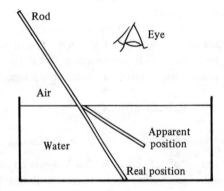

Figure 8.4

Examples

1. A ray of light is incident at an angle of 60° in air on a block of glass; the angle of refraction is 40°. Calculate the refractive index.

$i = 60°$
$r = 40°$

Refractive index $\mu = \dfrac{\sin i}{\sin r}$

$$= \dfrac{\sin 60°}{\sin 40°} = \dfrac{0.8660}{0.6428} = 1.35$$

The refractive index is 1.35.

2. Draw a ray diagram when a ray of light is passing from air to glass with an angle of incidence of 50°. The refractive index of glass is 1.5.

$\mu = 1.5$
$i = 50°$

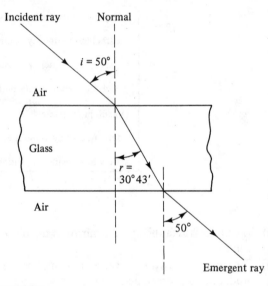

Figure 8.5

$$\mu = \dfrac{\sin i}{\sin r} \quad \text{and} \quad \sin r = \dfrac{\sin i}{\mu} = \dfrac{\sin 50°}{1.5}$$

$$= \dfrac{0.7660}{1.5} = 0.5107$$

Therefore $r = \sin^{-1} 0.5107 = 30°43'$.

3. The apparent depth of a quantity of liquid was 145 millimetres when its real depth was 250 millimetres. Determine the index of refraction given

that index of refraction = real depth/apparent depth.

Real depth = 250 mm
Apparent depth = 145 mm

$$\mu = \frac{\text{real depth}}{\text{apparent depth}} = \frac{250}{145} = 1.72$$

The index of refraction is 1.72.

8.6 Lenses

A lens is a piece of transparent material, usually of glass but sometimes of plastic or quartz, bounded by two surfaces of regular curvature. The purpose of a lens is to change the curvature of wavefronts so that the light waves may be focused to a desired position. There are a variety of types; we shall concentrate on two.

(a) Convex lens – the lens is thicker at the centre than at the edges, as shown in Fig. 8.6. If a parallel beam of light is incident on a small central portion of the lens, the rays converge to a point F on the principal axis of the lens. The principal focus F is the point through which all rays entering the lens parallel to the principal axis pass after refraction. For a thin lens the focal length f may be taken as the distance from the principal focus to the centre of the lens.

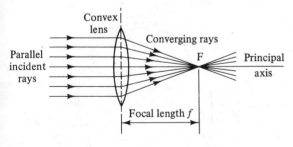

Figure 8.6

(b) Concave lens – the lens is thinner at the centre than at the edges, as shown in Fig. 8.7. If parallel rays are incident on the lens from right to left, the rays diverge after refraction and appear to come from the point F on the principal axis. Again F is the principal focus and for a thin lens the focal length is the distance from f to the centre of the lens.

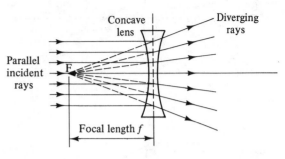

Figure 8.7

Lenses are used in many everyday articles such as spectacles, microscopes, telescopes, binoculars, film projectors, and cameras.

8.7 Formation of an image by a thin convex lens

The image produced by a thin convex lens varies in nature and relative size with the position of the object as shown in Fig. 8.8. From the figures it can be seen that when an object is a long way from the lens a real inverted image is formed. As the object approaches the lens, the image becomes larger, but it is real and inverted until the object reaches the principal focus, at which point the image is an infinite distance from the lens. When the object is at a position less than the focal length, a magnified, erect, virtual image is formed.

8.8 Formation of an image by a thin concave lens

Unlike a convex lens, the image obtained with a concave lens is always virtual, erect, and smaller than the object, no matter where the object is placed, as shown in Fig. 8.9.

8.9 Human eye

The eye contains a convex lens which is able to change its curvature so as to adjust the focus. It focuses

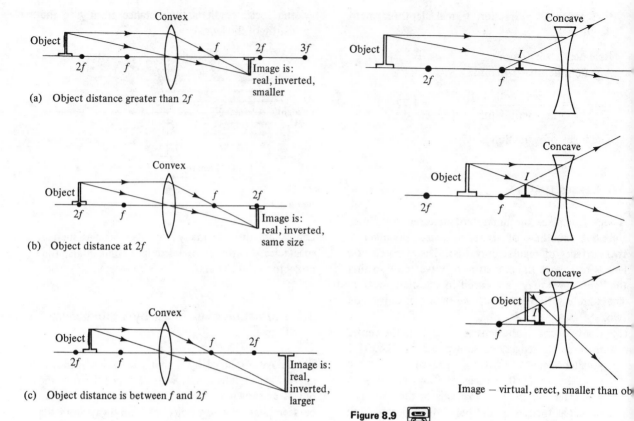

(a) Object distance greater than 2f

Image is: real, inverted, smaller

(b) Object distance at 2f

Image is: real, inverted, same size

(c) Object distance is between f and 2f

Image is: real, inverted, larger

Image – virtual, erect, smaller than ob

Figure 8.9

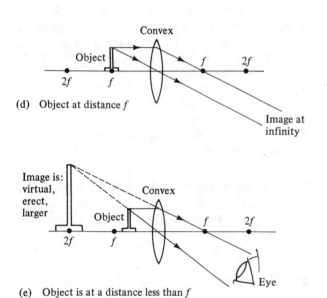

(d) Object at distance f

Image at infinity

Image is: virtual, erect, larger

(e) Object is at a distance less than f

Eye

Figure 8.8

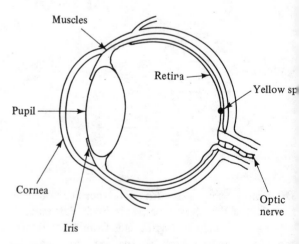

Muscles

Retina

Yellow sp

Pupil

Cornea

Iris

Optic nerve

Figure 8.10

images on the retina for objects at different distances from the eye. The retina is a light-sensitive membrane at the back of the eye chamber, as shown in Fig. 8.10.

The image is real, inverted, and smaller than the object, but the brain interprets the message in such a way that the object is seen as being the right way up. The iris, in front of the lens, is a circular diaphragm which opens and closes according to the intensity of light received. The central aperture is called the pupil. The part of the outer surface of the eye which is immediately in front of the iris is transparent and is called the cornea. The most light-sensitive spot on the retina and the centre for direct vision is called the yellow spot.

Two common defects of the eye are long sight and short sight. A person with long sight is unable to see objects that are close, as the cornea has insufficient curvature and/or the eyeball is too short for the rays from the object to be focused on the retina; instead they are focused on a point behind the retina, as shown in Fig. 8.11. This defect of vision is corrected by the use of a convex lens as shown in Fig. 8.12. The convex lens causes light rays to converge before they reach the cornea, so that the focus on the retina is restored.

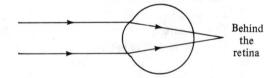

Figure 8.11

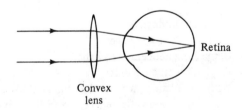

Figure 8.12

A person with short sight is unable to focus distant objects as the cornea has too great a curvature or the eyeball is too long. Rays are brought to a focus at a point in front of the retina, as shown in Fig. 8.13. This defect is corrected by using a concave lens, as

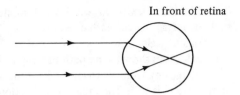

In front of retina

Figure 8.13

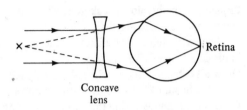

Concave lens

Figure 8.14

shown in Fig. 8.14 where parallel light incident on the lens diverges before reaching the cornea, so that focus on the retina is again restored.

8.10 Exercise

1. State the two laws of reflection for a plane mirror.
2. Explain with the aid of a sketch whether the image in a plane mirror is real or virtual.
3. Show with the aid of a diagram that the image in a plane mirror and the object are at equal distances from the mirror.
4. Draw a ray diagram for a plane mirror with the angle of reflection equal to $70°$. Label the angle of reflection and the angle of incidence.
5. Draw a sketch showing the incident and refracted rays for light undergoing refraction from air to glass.
6. A ray of light is incident at an angle of $55°$ in air on a block of glass with an angle of refraction of $30°$. Calculate the refractive index.
7. A ray of light is incident in water at an angle of $35°$ on the plane boundary with air. Determine the angle of refraction if the refractive index of water is 1.3.
8. Describe, with the aid of a sketch, a method of measuring the refractive index of glass in the form of a rectangular block.
9. A ray of light travelling in glass strikes its surface, making an angle of incidence of $40°$ and $60°$. If

the refractive index of glass is 1.5 determine the angle of refraction for each case; then draw both situations to scale.

10. Draw a diagram showing the path of a ray of light which is passing from air to glass where the angle of refraction is 25°. The index of refraction for glass is 1.4. Calculate the value of the angle of incidence.

11. Explain, with the aid of a sketch, why a pool of water appears shallower than it really is.

12. Explain, with the aid of a sketch, the difference between a convex and a concave lens.

13. Draw a sketch illustrating the subsequent path of a parallel beam of light incident on a convex lens.

14. Draw a sketch illustrating the subsequent path of a parallel beam of light incident on a concave lens.

15. Explain what is meant by the terms 'principal focus' and 'focal length' of a convex and concave lens.

16. Why is a convex lens often called a converging lens and a concave lens called a diverging lens?

17. An object 20 mm high is placed in front of a convex lens of focal length 50 mm. Draw to scale a ray diagram to show the image formed and obtain the position and size of the image for the following object distances: (a) 100 mm, (b) 75 mm, (c) 50 mm, (d) 25 mm.

18. Draw diagrams to illustrate how a convex lens can be used to produce a magnified image: (a) which is real and (b) which is virtual.

19. An object 15 mm high is placed 25 mm from a concave lens of focal length 20 mm. Determine graphically the position and size of the image.

20. After discussion with your class teacher explain with the aid of sketches how you would determine experimentally the focal length of a thin convex lens.

21. Describe, with the aid of a well-labelled sketch, a simple model of the human eye.

22. Explain what is meant by the term 'short sight' and how it can be corrected by the use of a lens.

23. Explain what is meant by the term 'long sight' and how it can be corrected by the use of a lens.

24. After discussion with your class teacher write out a list of uses of convex and concave lenses.

25. Complete the crossword puzzle of Fig. 8.15 using Chapter 8 as reference material.

Figure 8.15

Across

6. Angle of . . . . equals angle of reflection.
7. Convex or concave nearly
8. . . . of light
10. Type of image
11. Electromagnetic radiation
12. Refractive . . . . . = sin i/sin r
14. Type of mirror
15. The last three letters of beam

Down

1. Measured in degrees
2. Almost a type of image
3. Something happening to light
4. Angle of incidence unit
5. With a plane mirror; the incident ray, ... , and reflected ray lie in the same plane.
8. Symbol for angle of refraction
9. Part of an image
10. Part of the spectrum or blood-like
11. The first three letters of velocity but in reverse
13. We see with it.

Figure 8.16

12. The angle of incidence with the . . . . . . is equal to the angle of reflection.
13. A spot in conjunction with 16 across

Figure 8.17

26. Complete the crossword puzzle of Fig. 8.16 using Chapter 8 as reference material.

Across
4. This item is protected by a transparent layer of tissue called the cornea.
6. . . . . . of incidence = ... of reflection
8. A mixed-up 'f'
9. Something that the eye can see through
14. A sensitive lining of the back of the eye chamber
15. An abbreviation for millimetre
16. Part of a spot connected to 13 down and opposite to high
17. Another part of the eye protected by a transparent layer of tissue — but the word is mixed up

Down
1. The material of a lens
2. Part of magnification
3. The last three letters of image
4. A big image nearly
5. A plane mirror produces an . . . . . the same size as the object
7. Types are convex and concave
10. Usually a mirror
11. Electromagnetic . . .iation

27. Complete the crossword puzzle of Fig. 8.17 using Chapter 8 as reference material.

Across
1. Figure 8.2 opposite the object
4. Nothing to do with light — more to do with sound
6. A type of image
8. Incident is a type
9. A defect of sight
11. The image in a concave lens is always this.
12. Sensitive to light
14. Related to yellow
16. System of units
17. Con. .ve
18. The incident ray, ...al, and reflected ray lie in the same plane.

Down
1. Opposite of upright
2. A medium that light can pass through
3. See 16 across
4. Type of mirror

84

5. Unit of frequency
7. Principal . . . . .
9. Concave or convex
10. Ene. .y, but use the letters in reverse
13. Light and sound travel in this way, but reverse the word
15. $\sin^{-1} 0.1736 = ?$

Answers

Section 8.10
6. 1.64
7. $26°11'$
9. $25°22, 35°16'$
10. $36°16'$

9 Chemical processes

9.1 Elements

An element is a substance consisting entirely of atoms of the same atomic number, and which cannot be chemically broken down into any simpler substance. Examples of elements are shown in Table 9.1.

Table 9.1

Element	Symbol	Atomic number
Aluminium	Al	13
Arsenic	As	33
Barium	Ba	56
Carbon	C	6
Copper	Cu	29
Fluorine	F	9
Germanium	Ge	32
Gold	Au	79
Hydrogen	H	1
Iron	Fe	26
Lead	Pb	82
Mercury	Hg	80
Nitrogen	N	7
Oxygen	O	8
Platinum	Pt	78
Silicon	Si	14
Silver	Ag	47
Tin	Sn	50
Titanium	Ti	22
Tungsten	W	74
Uranium	U	92
Zinc	Zn	30

9.2 Compounds

A compound is a substance consisting of two or more elements chemically united in definite proportions. A chemical reaction is a process in which the atoms of one element become attached to atoms from another element to form a compound. An atom describes the smallest part of an element and a molecule describes the smallest part of either an element or a compound capable of independent existence. (Some molecules of elements are single atoms and some contain more than one atom.) Examples of diatomic molecules of elements are given in Table 9.2.

Table 9.2

Element	Atom	Molecule
Chlorine	Cl	Cl_2
Hydrogen	H	H_2
Oxygen	O	O_2
Nitrogen	N	N_2

9.3 Chemical equations

Chemical reactions involve the interactions between substances resulting in rearrangement of atoms involved into different molecules as shown in the following examples:

(a) Carbon + oxygen = carbon dioxide
$$C + O_2 = CO_2$$

(b) Hydrogen + oxygen = water
$$2H_2 + O_2 = 2H_2O$$
The $2H_2$ indicates two molecules of hydrogen, each of which contains two atoms, and $2H_2O$ indicates two molecules of water, each of which contains two atoms of hydrogen and one of oxygen.

(c) Copper + sulphur + oxygen = copper sulphate
$$Cu + S + 2O_2 = CuSO_4$$
In this case, one atom of copper combines with one atom of sulphur and two molecules of oxygen to produce copper sulphate.

9.4 Mixtures

A mixture contains a number of substances without any chemical reaction taking place. A mixture may be of solids, liquids, or gases.
Examples of mixtures are:
(a) tea, milk, and sugar,
(b) peas and beans,
(c) sulphur and iron filings,
(d) copper, zinc, and tin scrap,

(e) carbon dioxide and water in soda water.

The characteristics of mixtures are that the substances can at least in theory be physically separated, the proportions of the constituents can vary, and there is no production of heat on mixing.

9.5 Composition of the atmosphere

Air is a mixture of a number of gases, chiefly nitrogen and oxygen. The other gases which are present in much smaller proportions are carbon dioxide, argon, neon, helium, krypton, and xenon. The ratio of nitrogen to oxygen is about four to one.

9.6 Oxidation

Oxidation is the combination of oxygen with an element or the removal of hydrogen from it.

The following are examples of oxidation:

(a) Magnesium + oxygen = magnesium oxide

$$2Mg \quad + \quad O_2 \quad = \quad 2MgO$$

We have two molecules of magnesium combining with one molecule of oxygen to give two molecules of magnesium oxide.

(b) Copper + oxygen = copper oxide

$$2Cu \quad + \quad O_2 \quad = \quad 2CuO$$

In this case, two molecules of copper combine with one molecule of oxygen to give two molecules of copper oxide.

In each of the examples above it is very important to note that the metal extracts oxygen from the air and combines with this oxygen to form a compound, the mass of the resulting compound being greater than the original mass of the element.

9.7 Corrosion

Rust, or corrosion in general terms, is a hydrated oxide of iron, with the chemical formulae of $Fe_2O_3 \cdot H_2O$, formed on the surface of iron when it is exposed to moisture (i.e., water) and air (i.e., oxygen). Iron will not corrode in perfectly dry air or in water which is completely free from dissolved oxygen. Corrosion is thus a chemical reaction involving iron, water, and oxygen.

Damage done by corrosion can be extensive, typical examples being:

(a) damage to motor car bodies,

(b) crumbling of metal window frames,

(c) rusting of ships' hulls,

(d) corrosion of tin cans.

Some methods employed to combat corrosion are:

(a) covering the surface with paint,

(b) covering with a film of oil,

(c) covering with a zinc coating (galvanizing),

(d) electroplating.

9.8 Exercise

1. Define the following terms:
   (a) element, (b) compound, and (c) mixture.
2. Explain what is meant by the term 'chemical reaction'.
3. Give five examples of mixtures.
4. Define the term 'oxidation'.
5. Give two examples of oxidation.
6. Describe why a substance such as copper gains mass when heated in air so that oxygen is taken from the air by the copper.
7. Describe how oxygen and water are involved in the corrosion of iron.
8. After a discussion with your class teacher, give 10 examples of damage done by corrosion.
9. After a discussion with your class teacher and reference to trade literature state five methods used to prevent corrosion.
10. What is the approximate proportion of oxygen to nitrogen in the atmosphere?
11. Complete the crossword puzzle of Fig. 9.1 using Chapter 9 as reference material.

Across

1. An oxide is a compound of an element and . . . . . .
3. Opposite of dry
5. Oxidat.o.
7. The atmosphere surrounds it
8. An . . . . describes the smallest part of an element.
11. Fe/26

Figure 9.1

13. An example of a mixture — often taken in the afternoon
15. Opposite of 'yes'
17. Four-fifths of the atmosphere

19. Symbol for platinum
21. Almost water
24. An example of this is sulphur and iron filings

Down
1. Fe without the ir
2. A substance consisting entirely of atoms of the same atomic number
3. Something corrosion can do without
4. Symbol for titanium
5. A gas may fall into this category
6. Symbol for barium
9. See 4 down
10. Symbol for zinc
12. Atomic number for hydrogen
14. Opposite of full
16. Electrons are in this
18. Atomic number for fluorine — nearly
20. Silicon?
22. Copper symbol
23. Copp. .

10 Chemical effect of an electric current

10.1 Electrolysis

When an electric current flows through a conducting liquid, or electrolyte, chemical action takes place and the liquid is decomposed. Some electrolytes are better conductors than others, the most useful being acids, alkalis, or salts in liquid form or in solution in water. To allow the current to flow in and out of the electrolyte, metal electrodes are placed in it. Current flows through the positive electrode (anode), through the electrolyte, and out of the negative electrode (cathode). The nature of the chemical action remains unchanged regardless of the type of material used for the electrodes and the liquid used as the electrolyte. In general, the anode loses weight and the cathode gains weight during this process. This chemical action is called electrolysis.

10.2 Ionic theory

When an e.m.f. is applied to the metal electrodes immersed in an electrolyte, some of the molecules of the electrolyte split up into electrically charged particles called ions. There are positively charged ions and negatively charged ions. The positively charged metal ions are attracted to the cathode; the negatively charged non-metallic ions are attracted to the anode.

10.3 Principle of electrodeposition of metals

A practical application of the principle is the coating of the surface of a material with a layer of metal, either to improve its appearance or for protection.

Typical materials for use as anodes and electrolytic solutions are given in the table.

Anode	Electrolytic solution
Copper	Copper cyanide
Chromium	Chromium sulphate
Zinc	Zinc cyanide
Silver	Silver nitrate

When the anode is connected to the positive terminal and the cathode is connected to the negative terminal of a cell, positive ions flow from the electrolyte to the cathode, which is the object to be coated or electroplated. The negative non-metallic ions of the electrolyte flow to the anode and recombine to form complete molecules of the electrolyte.

The strength of the electrolyte thus remains the same but the anode loses weight.

10.4 Primary cell

The purpose of a primary cell is to provide electric current to an external circuit.

An early cell, discovered by Volta, consisted of a zinc cathode and a copper anode in an electrolyte of dilute sulphuric acid. The Daniell cell was developed from this simple cell as shown in outline in Fig. 10.1.

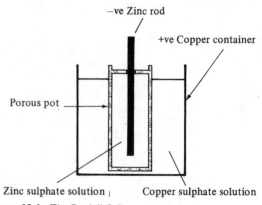

Figure 10.1 The Daniell Cell

The Leclanché cell developed in 1865 is shown in outline in Fig. 10.2. The e.m.f. of this cell is about 1.5 volts, but it falls off rapidly in use. Its main use was therefore on intermittent work.

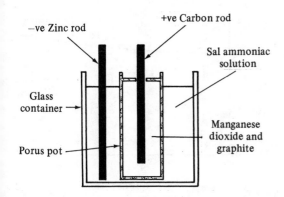

Figure 10.2 The Leclanché cell

The dry cell in use today is a development of the Leclanché wet cell. One such form consists of a zinc container, forming the negative electrode, lined with a paste of ammonium chloride and a substance similar to plaster of Paris, and having in the centre a carbon rod surrounded by a mixture of ammonium chloride, powdered carbon, zinc sulphate, and manganese dioxide made into a stiff paste. Its action is similar to that of the Leclanché cell giving an e.m.f. of about 1.5 volts. The dry cell is shown in outline form in Fig. 10.3.

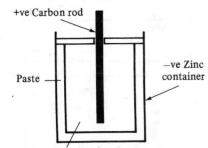

Mixture of ammonium chloride, powdered carbon, zinc sulphate, and manganese dioxide

Figure 10.3 A dry cell

A modern development in the primary cell field is the mercury cell shown in outline in Fig. 10.4.

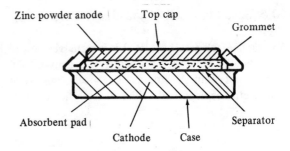

Figure 10.4 A mercury cell

The mild steel or stainless steel top cap is about 0.25 millimetre thick, and is sometimes nickel-plated. The absorbent pad contains an electrolyte of potassium hydroxide. The cathode is a mixture of mercuric oxide and graphite and is separated from the anode by an alkali-resisting paper. The advantage of this type of primary cell is its high ratio of energy to volume and weight and it can be made in a miniature form resulting in considerable saving in space. A popular use for this type of cell is in wristwatches and hearing aids. In industrial and commercial use it is of value in spacecraft and military devices.

A mercury cell having a diameter of 17 millimetres and a height of 17 millimetres has an e.m.f. of 1.4 volts when supplying a load current of 35 milliamperes giving a capacity of 1 ampere hour at this current.

When any primary cell is supplying current the electrodes and the electrolyte are gradually being used up and eventually they will supply no further current. When this stage is reached a primary cell is discarded, as it cannot be regenerated.

10.5 Secondary cell of the lead-acid type

A secondary cell is a cell which can be recharged after use. Probably the best known secondary cell is the lead-acid cell used in the construction of car batteries, which in fact is six lead-acid cells. Each lead-acid cell consists of two lead plates coated in lead sulphate immersed in a solution of sulphuric acid. When direct current is passed through the cell, the anode plate is converted to lead peroxide and the cathode plate is reduced to metallic lead. If the two plates are then connected to an external circuit, the chemical action is reversed and current flows round the external circuit.

10.6 Secondary cell of the alkaline type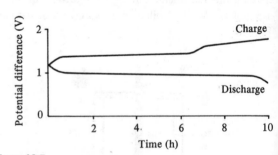

An alkaline cell (see Fig. 10.5) is a rechargeable cell using an alkaline electrolyte, which is usually a solution of potassium hydroxide. Each cell consists of two electrodes deposited in the electrolytic solution.

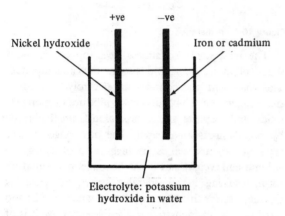

Figure 10.5 A nickel-iron or nickel-cadmium cell

To the family of alkaline cells belong:

> nickel-cadmium,
> nickel-iron,
> silver-zinc,
> silver-cadmium,
> nickel-zinc.

Each of the mentioned materials forms one of the electrodes. For an equivalent type of cell all of the above produce a lower e.m.f. than the lead-acid cell. A table of typical e.m.f.s is given below:

Cell	Electromotive force (V)
Nickel-cadmium	1.29
Nickel-iron	1.37
Silver-zinc	1.70
Silver-cadmium	1.20
Nickel-zinc	1.735

In general terms alkaline cells are more expensive than lead-acid cells for a similar capacity but they are lighter in weight yet more robust in construction than the lead-acid type of cell.

10.7 Typical charge and discharge curves for cells

Figure 10.6 shows charge and discharge curves for a lead-acid cell.

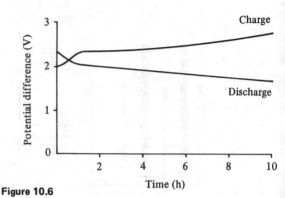

Figure 10.6

To charge a lead-acid cell a voltage greater than 2 volts is needed. On discharge the cell e.m.f. falls very rapidly to 2 volts. After this a gradual reduction takes place over a period of time depending upon the amount of current flowing.

Figure 10.7 shows charge and discharge curves for a nickel-alkaline cell.

The average charge voltage is about 1.5 volts with an average discharge of 1.2 volts at normal current.

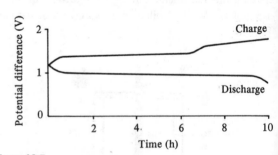

Figure 10.7

10.8 Capacity and efficiency

The efficiency of a cell is the ratio of capacity during discharge to capacity during charge:

$$\text{Efficiency} = \frac{\text{capacity during discharge}}{\text{capacity during charge}} \times 100\%$$

$$\text{Efficiency} = \frac{\begin{array}{c}\text{discharge current}\\ \times\\ \text{time taken during discharge}\end{array}}{\begin{array}{c}\text{charge current}\\ \times\\ \text{time taken during charge}\end{array}} \times 100\%$$

An alternative to the capacity efficiency is the watt hour efficiency:

$$\text{Efficiency} = \frac{\text{watt hours during discharge}}{\text{watt hours during charge}} \times 100\%$$

For a good lead-acid cell the ampere hour efficiency is about 80 per cent as compared with a watt hour efficiency of about 70 per cent.

Examples

1. Calculate the ampere hour efficiency of a battery that is fully charged after receiving a constant current of 10 amperes for 8 hours. The battery is completely discharged after supplying a steady current of 2 amperes for 30 hours.

$$\text{Efficiency} = \frac{\begin{array}{c}\text{discharge current}\\ \times\\ \text{time taken during discharge}\end{array}}{\begin{array}{c}\text{charge current}\\ \times\\ \text{time taken during charge}\end{array}} \times 100\%$$

$$= \frac{2 \times 30 \times 100}{10 \times 8}$$

$$= 75 \text{ per cent}$$

The ampere hour efficiency of the battery is 75 per cent.

2. A cell is fully discharged after supplying a current of 7.5 amperes for 10 hours at an average voltage of 1.9 volts. The cell is charged at 20 amperes for 5 hours with a mean voltage of 2.2 volts. Calculate the watt hour efficiency.

$$\text{Efficiency} = \frac{\text{watt hours during discharge}}{\text{watt hours during charge}} \times 100\%$$

$$= \frac{1.9 \times 7.5 \times 10 \times 100}{2.2 \times 20 \times 5}$$

$$= 64.77 \text{ per cent}$$

The watt hour efficiency of the cell is 64.77 per cent.

10.9 Exercise

1. Explain what is meant by the term 'electrolysis'.
2. State a practical application of the action of electrolysis.
3. Explain how in the process of electrolysis the strength of the electrolyte remains the same but the anode loses weight.
4. What electrolytic solution is used when the anode is made from copper?
5. State the purpose of a primary cell.
6. Sketch in outline of Leclanché cell.
7. State the e.m.f. of a Leclanché cell.
8. Draw a labelled diagram of a mercury cell.
9. State the chemical used as the electrolyte in a mercury cell.
10. Can a primary cell be recharged?
11. List the contents of a lead-acid cell.
12. Explain the fundamental difference between a primary cell and a secondary cell.
13. List five types of alkaline cells.
14. State typical e.m.f.s for a nickel-cadmium cell and a nickel-iron cell.
15. Sketch a typical charge and discharge curve for a lead-acid cell and an alkaline cell.
16. State two formulae for determining the efficiency of a cell.
17. Sketch in outline a typical dry cell.
18. A test on an alkaline cell gave the following results:

Duration of discharge (h)	1	2	3	4	5
Capacity (A h)	35	70	75	80	85

Plot a graph of duration of discharge against capacity. (WJEC)
19. A battery is fully discharged after supplying a load current of 2 A for 25 h. To fully recharge the battery a current of 10 A is needed for 6 h. Calculate the ampere hour efficiency.
20. A cell is fully discharged after supplying a current for 15 h. The normal rate of charge is 25 A for

92

4 h. If the efficiency is 80 per cent determine the discharge current.

21. A cell is fully charged after receiving 2 A for 10 h with a mean terminal voltage of 2.5 V. On discharge, the cell supplies current at the rate of 5 A for 4.5 h at a mean terminal voltage of 2 V. Calculate the watt hour efficiency.

22. An alkaline cell is discharged at a steady current of 4 A for 12 h, the average terminal voltage being 1.2 V. To restore it to its original state of charge, a steady current of 3 A for 20 h is required, the average terminal voltage being 1.44 V. Calculate the ampere hour and watt hour efficiencies in this particular case.   (NWRAC)

23. An emergency battery has 175 alkaline cells connected in series and the input capacity is 1000 A h. If the quantity efficiency is 80 per cent, calculate the power consumed during an 8-hour discharge if the average voltage during discharge is 1.2 V per cell.   (WMAC)

24. Complete the crossword puzzle of Fig. 10.8 by using Chapter 10 as reference material.

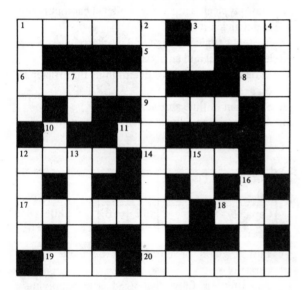

Figure 10.8

Across
1. Often an electrolyte
3. Circuit current will not flow with a switch in this position.
5. See Sec. 10.2, electrically charged particle
6. Positive
8. Alternating current
9. Delivers a force
11. Abbreviation for ampere hour
12. To operate, circuits must be in this condition
14. Used as a dilute liquid in secondary cells
17. The value for a mercury cell is 1.4.
18. Calculate the ampere hour efficiency of a battery that is fully charged after receiving a constant current of 10 A for 10 h. The battery is completely discharged after supplying a steady current of 2 A for 45 h. (To complete the clue deduce the calculated efficiency from 100.)
19. Many lead-acid cells are used in these.
20. Strength of acid used in some types of cell

Down
1. A material used for the plates in a cell
2. An empty cell
3. Opposite to 'off'
4. One type of alkaline cell
7. The last two letters of duration
10. A system of units
12. See 12 across.
13. Discovered a cell
15. Formula for capacity during discharge
16. An effect of an electric current

Answers

Section 10.9
10. No
19. 83.33%
20. 5.33 A
21. 90%
22. 80%, 66.66%
23. 21 kW

11 Investigations

Investigation 11.1

To determine the relationship between force and extension for given materials.

Equipment: Length of rubber
Coil of copper wire
Retort stands
Weights
Measurement card

Diagram:

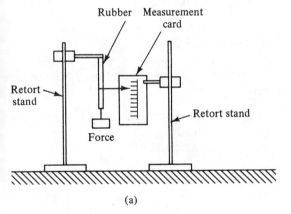

(a)

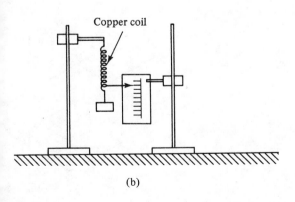

(b)

Figure 11.1

Method:
(a) Set up the equipment using the length of rubber as shown in Fig. 11.1(a).
(b) Add the weights one at a time and note the extension produced.
(c) Remove the weights one at a time and note the position of the pointer.
(d) Record your results in a table similar to the one drawn below.
(e) Plot a graph from the results showing the relationship between force applied and extension.
(f) Repeat items (a) to (e) using the coil of copper wire as in Fig. 11.1(b).

Results:

Force					
Extension: increasing					
Extension: decreasing					

Discussion:
(a) Did both materials stretch under the applied force?
(b) Which material stretched the most?
(c) What happened to each material when the applied force was removed?
(d) Did either graph follow a straight line?
(e) Was Hooke's law found to be true for both materials?

Investigation 11.2

To determine the centre of mass of an irregular sheet.

Equipment: Drawing board
Backing sheet
Lamina
Drawing pins and twine
Pencil
Rule

Diagram:

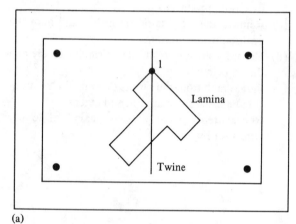

(a)

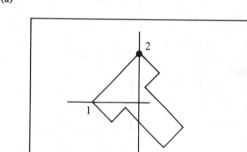

(b)

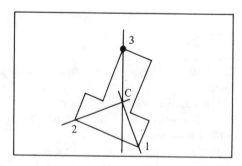

(c)

Figure 11.2

Method:
(a) Stand the drawing board vertically and pin to it the backing sheet.
(b) Examine the lamina and check that it has at least three small holes drilled in its periphery.
(c) Using the twine and pins, suspend the lamina from one hole as shown in Fig. 11.2(a).
(d) With the pencil and rule carefully draw a line following the direction of the twine.
(e) Repeat (c) and (d) for the other two holes. (Fig. 11.2(b), (c).)
(f) The vertical lines should all cross at a single point which is termed the centre of mass.

Results:
Record your result by drawing a small-scale diagram of your lamina and indicating the position of the centre of mass.

Discussion:
Comment upon any difficulties that you encountered during this investigation.

Investigation 11.3

To determine the value of speed from a distance–time graph.

Equipment: Trolley and plank
Weights
Timing device

Diagram:

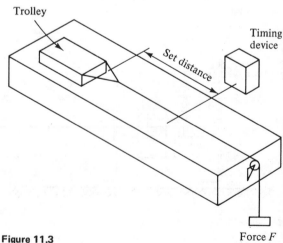

Figure 11.3

Method:
(a) Set up the equipment as shown in Fig. 11.3.
(b) Try a number of trial runs by releasing the trolley and observing the effect.
(c) Adjust the level of the plane until the trolley just moves freely; this is to cancel the effects of friction between the trolley and the plank.
(d) Decide on a fixed distance and take this measurement from the front of the trolley. At the end point of this fixed distance place in position your timing device.
(e) Place a small weight in position F and let the trolley go. Note the time taken to cover the distance.
(f) Repeat (d) and (e) for different fixed distances.

Results:

Distance						
Time		.				

Graph: Plot a graph of distance against time and from it determine the slope; this is the speed of the trolley.

Discussion:
(a) State the value of speed obtained.
(b) Comment upon any difficulties encountered during this investigation.
(c) Make suggestions for improving the timing of each run.

Investigation 11.4

To measure the refractive index of glass.

Equipment: Glass block
Sheet of paper
Light box

Diagram:

Method:
(a) Place the glass block on the sheet of paper and draw round its edges with a pencil.
(b) Switch on the light box and adjust it until a single narrow beam strikes the glass block at an angle as shown in Fig. 11.4.

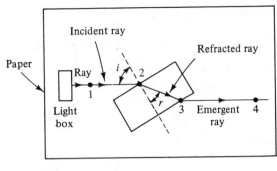

i = angle at incidence
r = angle of refraction

Figure 11.4

(c) Mark with a pencil points 1, 2, 3, and 4.
(d) Switch off the light source, remove the glass block, and join up points 1, 2, 3, and 4.
(e) Measure the angle of incidence and the angle of refraction.
(f) Tabulate the results and calculate the refractive index.
(g) Repeat items (a) to (f) for different angles of incidence.
(h) Determine the mean value of the refractive index by the investigation.

Results:

Angle of incidence (i)				
Angle of refraction (r)				
Sin i				
Sin r				
Refractive index μ				

Mean value for refractive index = ...

Discussion:
(a) State the value of the refractive index found and compare it to the known value for glass.
(b) Comment upon any difficulties encountered during this investigation.

Investigation 11.5

To determine the focal length of a thin convex lens.

Equipment: Convex lens with holder
Supported plane mirror
Light source object and screen
Metre rule

Diagram:

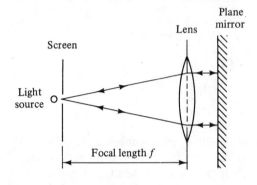

Figure 11.5

Method:
(a) Set up the lens and plane mirror as shown in Fig. 11.5.
(b) Switch on the light source to illuminate the object.
(c) Adjust the object forwards and backwards until a sharp image is formed on the screen alongside the object.
(d) Measure the distance from the object to the lens.
(e) The measurement in (d) is the focal length and can be recorded.
(f) Repeat (a) to (e) for different lenses.

Results:

Lens	1	2	3	4	5
Focal length (mm)					

Discussion:
(a) Comment upon the values found for each lens.
(b) Comment upon any difficulties encountered during the investigation.
(c) After a discussion with your class teacher explain why point O is the principal focus of the lens.

Investigation 11.6

To determine the form of a temperature–time graph for a substance which changes its state during the investigation.

Equipment: Naphthalene
Test tube
Thermometer
Retort stand
Bunsen burner
Stop watch

Diagram:

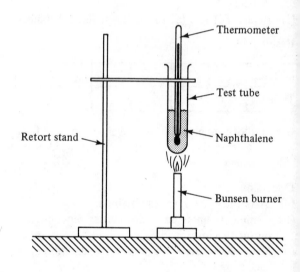

Figure 11.6

Method:
(a) Half fill the test tube with solid naphthalene and heat it gently in the set-up shown in Fig. 11.6 until it has completely melted.
(b) Place the thermometer into the melted naphthalene and note the initial temperature.
(c) Read the temperature at fixed intervals of time.
(d) Note the results in the table below.
(e) Plot a graph of temperature against time.

Results:

Temperature (°C)						
Time (s)						

Discussion:
(a) Comment on the shape of the graph obtained.
(b) From the graph read off the melting point of naphthalene.
(c) Comment upon any difficulties you encountered during this investigation.
(d) Indicate on the graph the section that corresponds to sensible heat and latent heat.

Investigation 11.7

The charge and discharge of a secondary cell.

Equipment: Discharged secondary cell
Voltmeter
Ammeter
Hydrometer
Timing device
Variable resistor
Direct current supply
Lamp
Single-pole switch

Diagram:

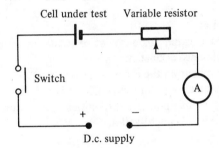

Cell under test   Variable resistor

Switch

A

+   −

D.c. supply

Figure 11.7

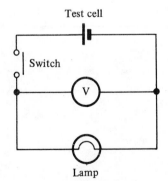

Test cell

Switch

V

Lamp

Figure 11.8

Method:
(a) Connect up the given components as shown in Fig. 11.7.
(b) Measure the relative density (specific gravity) of the cell using the hydrometer and note the result.
(c) Close the switch, adjust the current to an appropriate value, and charge the cell for a period of time.
(d) During the charging period note the voltmeter reading at fixed intervals of time. Take care to adjust the variable resistor to give the original value of current if this varies during charge. Record all readings.
(e) When the cell is fully charged switch off and note the colour of the plates.
(f) Disconnect the circuit.
(g) Connect up the given components as shown in Fig. 11.8.
(h) Measure the relative density of the electrolyte and note the result.
(i) Switch on and note the voltmeter reading for fixed intervals of time. Record all readings.
(j) Continue with the investigation until the lamp goes out.
(k) Switch off, disconnect the circuit, measure the relative density of the cell, and note the colour of the plates.

Results:
Relative density: Discharge value =
Charged value =
Discharged value =
Colour of plates: Fully charged . . . .
Discharged . . . .

Charging circuit:

Voltmeter reading						
Time						

Discharge circuit:

Voltmeter reading						
Time						

Discussion:
(a) Draw graphs of voltage against time for charge and discharge.

(b) Comment on the shape of each graph.

(c) Discuss why there is a difference in the relative density at the beginning and end of charge.

(d) Comment upon the colour of the plates at the beginning and end of charge.

Investigation 11.8

To investigate the relationship between potential difference and current for (a) a single resistor and (b) a non-linear component.

Equipment: Direct current variable supply
Ammeter
Voltmeter
Single-pole switch
Resistor
Lamp

Diagram:

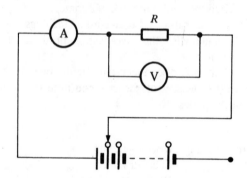

Figure 11.9

Method:

(a) Connect up the given components as shown i Fig. 11.9.

(b) Set the d.c. supply to its lowest value.

(c) Switch on and note the readings on the ammete and voltmeter.

(d) Repeat (b) and (c) for different settings of th d.c. supply.

(e) Replace the resistor with the lamp and repeat (b to (d).

(f) Tabulate all results.

Results:

Linear component — resistor

Voltmeter reading							
Ammeter reading							

Non-linear component — lamp

Voltmeter reading							
Ammeter reading							

Discussion:

(a) Plot a graph for each set of results of potential difference against current.

(b) Comment on the shape of each graph.

(c) Does either graph follow Ohm's law?

(d) Comment upon any difficulties you encountered during this investigation.

Solutions for technical crossword puzzles

Figure 1.30

Figure 2.7

Figure 1.31

Figure 3.7

Figure 2.6

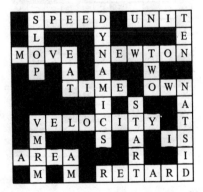

Figure 4.8

100

Figure 5.5

Figure 6.5

Figure 7.28

Figure 7.29

Figure 8.15

Figure 8.16

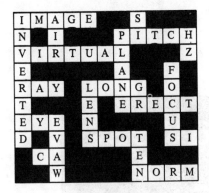

Figure 8.17

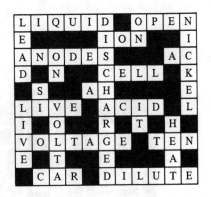

Figure 10.8

Figure 9.1